Caring for the Person with Dementia

Underpinning knowledge for frontline workers in adult social care

Malcolm Day

Pavilion

Caring for the Person with Dementia

Underpinning knowledge for frontline workers in adult social care

Published by:
Pavilion Publishing (Brighton) Ltd – part of OLM Group
Richmond House
Richmond Road
Brighton
BN2 3RL
UK

Tel: 01273 623222
Fax: 01273 625526
Email: info@pavpub.com
Web: www.pavpub.com

First published 2009, reprinted 2010.

A Catalogue reference for this book is available from the British Library.

ISBN: 978-1-84196-255-9

Pavilion is the leading training and development provider and publisher in the health, social care and allied fields, providing a range of innovative training solutions underpinned by sound research and professional values. We aim to put our customers first, through excellent customer service and good value.

Editor: Sanaz Nazemi, Pavilion
Cover design: Katherine Jones, Pavilion
Page layout and typesetting: Emma Garbutt, Pavilion
Printed on paper from a sustainable resource by: Ashford Press

Contents

About the author

Malcolm Day is a registered nurse and a registered practice educator. He is a Fellow of the Royal Society for Public Health, a Fellow of the Institute for Learning and a Fellow of the Higher Education Academy. Malcolm has previously held university lectureships in nursing, community care, and care management. Malcolm is co-author of ***Supporting People in their Own Homes, Safeguarding Vulnerable Adults,*** and ***Caring for the Older Person***, also published by Pavilion.

About this training resource

The way that qualifications are organised and structured within the social care sector is changing. By the latter part of 2010, the current National Qualifications Framework (NQF) will be replaced by the Qualification and Credit Framework (QCF).

The QCF is a new flexible way of recognising and rewarding skills and qualifications. It will present units and qualifications in a simpler way and it will lead to qualifications that are flexible and meet the skills and knowledge needs of the social care workforce.

According to Skills for Care (2009) every unit and qualification within the QCF will have a credit value and a level indicating how difficult it is.

Also, Skills for Care (2009) have indicated that there will be three sizes of qualifications within the QCF:

- awards (1 to 12 credits)
- certificates (13 to 36 credits)
- diplomas (37 credits or more).

In addition, Skills for Care (2009) have stated that each qualification will indicate:

- the level of the qualification, for example level 8 is the highest level
- the size of qualification, for example whether it is an award, certificate or diploma
- details outlining the content of the qualification.

Skills for Care have indicated that qualifications for dementia care will feature in the new QCF and are already planning the level, size and content of these new qualifications – based on the work they previously completed for the dementia care knowledge set. This training resource draws upon the previous work undertaken by Skills for Care to identify underpinning knowledge for the new dementia care qualifications that will appear within the new QCF. It will be of value to new workers entering the social care sector, as well social care workers who are continually developing their knowledge within the field of dementia care.

Throughout this training resource, there are ☺ learning activities for you to complete, which introduce you to the key aspects that are going to be covered. You should complete these before you commence or continue your reading and discuss them with a colleague or your supervisor. At the end of each chapter there is a quiz to help you revise the knowledge that has been covered. The answers to the learning activities and the quizzes are provided in the **appendix**.

At the end of each chapter, there is also a continuing professional development (CPD) log ✍ for you to complete with your supervisor. This is particularly important if you intend to undertake the new dementia care qualifications as you can be given credit for any prior learning you have undertaken – based on the content, number of hours and level of study you have completed.

The CPD log will also assist your manager to keep a record of your training, which is a requirement of your social care inspectorate and the Care Quality Council.

Chapter one

Defining dementia

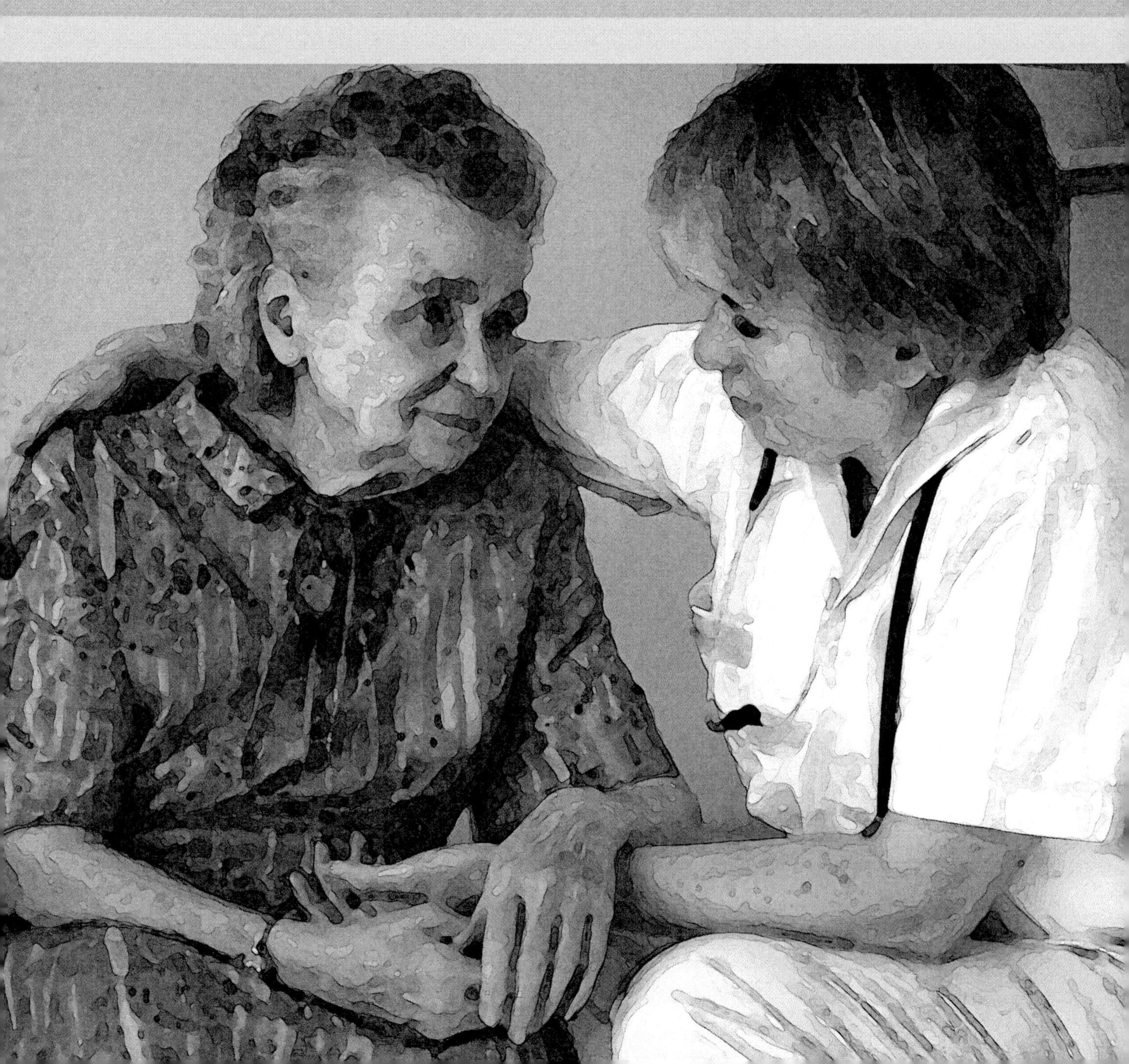

Chapter one

Defining dementia

☺ Key learning activity

This activity will provide you with key background information before you read **chapter one**. Make a note of your answers and discuss these with a colleague or your supervisor before you commence with your reading.

Q. Go to www.alzheimers.org.uk and click on 'about dementia'. Then click on 'factsheets'. Finally, click on 'What is dementia? Factsheet 400'.

- How many people in the UK have dementia?
- What are the four main types of dementia?
- What is mild cognitive impairment?
- Can dementia be cured?
- Can dementia be prevented?

AIMS OF THE CHAPTER

At the end of this chapter, the learner will be able to:

1. define the term 'dementia' and be able to differentiate this from other confusing states
2. outline the most common types and causes of dementia, for example, Alzhiemer's disease; vascular disease; Lewy body and Pick's disease
3. describe the signs and symptoms of dementia and the physical, emotional and social effects this may have on the individual, for example, decline in memory; decline in reasoning and communication; changes in behaviour; loss of skills to carry out normal daily activities etc
4. explain how a diagnosis of dementia is made and the implications this has for the support and care of an individual.

WHAT IS DEMENTIA?

According to the Alzheimer's Society, there are about 700,000 people in the UK with dementia. Dementia mainly affects older people, but it is estimated that there are some 15,000 people in the UK under the age of 65 who also have dementia (Alzheimer's Society, 2009a).

Generally speaking, the term 'dementia' is used to describe the symptoms that occur when the brain is affected by a specific condition or disease. There are over a 100 different conditions that can cause dementia. Some of the main ones include:

- Alzheimer's disease
- Lewy bodies disease
- vascular disease
- Parkinson's disease
- Pick's disease
- Huntingdon's disease
- Creutzfeldt–Jakob disease (CJD)
- HIV
- schizophrenia.

THE EFFECTS OF DEMENTIA ON THE INDIVIDUAL

Dementia is an insidious and progressive illness, which means the symptoms are slow to develop and steadily get worse over time. The way in which the disease progresses varies from individual to individual, as each person is unique and will experience the disease in their own way.

Many people with dementia will have a combination of conditions, which may be referred to as a dementia syndrome. Doctors can make a diagnosis of dementia based on the symptoms the individual may have, and a brain scan will confirm the diagnosis.

The damage to certain areas of the brain will cause the functions of those areas to become impaired. Therefore, the symptoms of dementia are dependent on the individual sufferer's experience. For example, one individual may not be able to think clearly while another may be unable to remember recent events or the names of people close to them.

Other people tend to notice signs of impairment by recognising the difficulties that an individual may have in their actions or behaviour. For example, others may notice that the individual has difficulty in getting dressed or writing a shopping list.

These impairments in brain function can affect an individual's:

- memory
- reasoning
- orientation
- recognition of people or objects

- speech and language
- planning and sequencing the stages of a task or activity
- judgement and safety awareness.

These impairments will eventually cause the individual to become disabled in undertaking everyday tasks, and in communicating with other people. For example, difficulty with:

- hygiene may be the result of impaired memory and reasoning
- finding their way home may be the result of impaired orientation
- eating a meal may be the result of impaired recognition of objects
- paying a bill may be the result of impaired speech and language
- dressing may be due to impaired sequencing of tasks and activities
- crossing the road may be due to impaired judgement and safety awareness.

In the later stages, a person with dementia will become increasingly dependent on other people to assist them with carrying out these activities.

Most forms of dementia are incurable. However, some types of dementia can be controlled and drugs have been developed to give some temporary relief from symptoms. These drugs are collectively known as acetyl cholinesterase inhibitors. The National Institute for Health and Clinical Excellence (NICE) recommends that people in the moderate stages of some types of dementia should be given treatment with one of these drugs.

According to the Alzheimer's Society (2009a) some individuals may have difficulty remembering to do things, but their symptoms may not be as severe as some forms of dementia. This condition is known as 'mild cognitive impairment' (MCI). A small number of people with MCI will have an increased risk of progressing to a dementia-type illness. However, a diagnosis of MCI does not always mean that the person will go on to develop full-blown dementia.

CASE STUDY: WHEN I FIRST REALISED THAT SOMETHING WAS WRONG

'One day I went out with odd shoes on. I tried to hide it. I thought, shall I take them off and go barefoot? It was a new style! You've got to laugh about it.'

*'I was talking with a consultant at the hospital. He was a crafty b******. He slipped a question into an ordinary conversation – "By the way Charlie, can you spell world?" and a bit later, "Can you spell world backwards?" I knew something was wrong.'*

'I was getting dressed one morning and I had put my shirt on the wrong way round, then I did it the next day and my wife said that I should go to the doctor, he sent me for a scan, that was the start of my memory problems.'

'I would go to the shops with a list of things to buy. However, I would return home with some wrong items.'

'My wife and I go every year to the same hotel in Spain. Then one year, I could not remember where anything was – the bar, the dining room, the swimming pool etc.'

'I am a sailor at heart, so I was always aboard ships. One day, I looked at one of the log books on a ship and I found that I could not understand what was on the page. I found this very frightening. Not being able to read anymore is a huge loss for me, as reading was something I really enjoyed.'

'Several of us found that we easily got distracted and had difficulty in finding the right word.'

'I first realised something was wrong when I first experienced problems with tasks I used to do everyday.'

When I first realised that something was wrong **(Alzheimer's Forum, 2004)**

THE MOST COMMON TYPES OF DEMENTIA

Alzheimer's disease

This is the most common cause of dementia, and according to the Alzheimer's Society (2009b) around 417,000 people in the UK have this disease. Alzheimer's disease was first described by the German neurologist Alois Alzheimer, and it is a physical disease where 'plaques' and 'tangles' develop in the structure of the brain, leading to the death of brain cells. People with Alzheimer's also have a shortage of some important chemicals in their brain. These chemicals are involved with the transmission of messages within the brain.

There is no known cause for Alzheimer's disease. Rather, it is thought that a combination of factors, including age, genetic inheritance, environmental factors, diet and overall general health are responsible. For example, because of the difference in their chromosomes, older people with Down's syndrome may develop Alzheimer's disease. People who have had severe head or whiplash injuries are also at increased risk of developing dementia. Research has also shown that people who smoke, and those who have high blood pressure or a high cholesterol level have an increased risk of developing Alzheimer's disease.

Alzheimer's is a progressive and debilitating disease and gradually over time, more parts of the brain become damaged. People in the early stages of Alzheimer's disease may experience lapses of memory and often have problems finding the right words. However, as the disease progresses, they may also:

- **become confused** and forget the names of people, places, appointments and recent events

- **experience mood swings;** they may feel sad, angry or scared; they may become frustrated by their increasing memory loss
- **become more withdrawn;** this may be caused by a loss of confidence or communication problems.

As the disease progresses, people with Alzheimer's disease need more and more support from those who care for them and eventually they need help with all their daily living activities, for example, eating and drinking, dressing, mobility, elimination etc.

There is no cure for Alzheimer's disease. However, some drug treatments are available that can relieve the symptoms or slow down the disease. For example, people with Alzheimer's have been shown to have a shortage of the chemical acetylcholine in their brains. The drugs donepezil hydrochloride, rivastigmine and galantamine work by maintaining existing supplies of acetylcholine. These drugs are available to people in the moderate stages of dementia.

Finally, the Alzheimer's Society (2009e) state that there is some evidence to suggest that dietary supplements of antioxidants, such as vitamins D and C can reduce the incidence of Alzheimer's.

Dementia with Lewy bodies

Dementia with Lewy bodies (DLB) is a form of dementia that accounts for around four per cent of all cases of dementia in older people. According to the Alzheimer's Society (2009c), DLB appears to affect men and women equally and is more common in people over the age of 65. However, in certain rare cases people under 65 may develop DLB.

Lewy bodies are named after the doctor who first identified them in 1912. They are small protein deposits found in nerve cells. Their presence in the brain disrupts the brain's normal functioning, interrupting the action of important chemical messengers, including acetylcholine and dopamine.

Lewy bodies are also found in the brains of people with Parkinson's disease – a progressive disorder of the nervous system that affects movement. Some people with Parkinson's disease may go on to develop symptoms that are very similar to DLB. People with DLB may generally experience:

- problems with attention and alertness
- spatial disorientation
- difficulty with planning ahead
- difficulty in co-ordinating mental activities
- memory loss, but less so than in Alzheimer's disease.

A person with DLB may also develop the symptoms of Parkinson's disease, including slowness, muscle stiffness, trembling of the limbs, a tendency to shuffle when walking, loss of facial expression and changes in the strength and tone of the voice.

In addition to the above, there are some characteristic symptoms that all DLB sufferers experience. These include:

- visual hallucinations
- fluctuation of physical and mental abilities often on an hourly or daily basis
- falling asleep very easily during the day with restless and disturbed nights characterised by confusion, nightmares and hallucinations
- frequent faints and falls.

There is no cure for DLB. The Alzheimer's Society (2009f) refers to research that suggests cholinesterase inhibitor drugs could be used. However, this is controversial and is governed by strict guidelines laid down by NICE.

People with DLB who are experiencing symptoms of Parkinson's disease may benefit from anti-Parkinson's drugs, although these can make hallucinations and confusion worse. Physiotherapy and mobility aids also help alleviate the stiffness and rigidity associated with Parkinson's disease.

When caring for someone with DLB, it is important to bear in mind that the symptoms of DLB will fluctuate over the course of a day. Therefore, care planning and delivery needs to be flexible.

Fronto-temporal dementia

Fronto-temporal dementia is a form of dementia that includes conditions such as Pick's disease. It occurs less frequently than other conditions such as Alzheimer's disease and according to the Alzheimer's Society (2009d) it is more likely to affect younger people under the age of 65 and is slightly more common in men.

The disease causes damage to the frontal lobe and temporal parts of the brain. These areas are responsible for our behaviour, emotional responses and language skills. As a consequence the symptoms are more often related to personality and behaviour changes, rather than loss of memory. For example, during the initial stages of this disease, the person's memory is still intact but they may:

- appear selfish and unfeeling
- become extrovert when they were previously introverted, or withdrawn when they were previously outgoing
- behave inappropriately, for example, making tactless comments, joking at the 'wrong' moments, or being rude
- lose their inhibitions – for example, exhibiting sexual behaviour in public
- become aggressive
- be easily distracted
- develop compulsive rituals and routines.

The person with fronto-temporal dementia may also experience language difficulties, including:

- problems finding the right words
- a lack of spontaneous conversation
- using many words to describe something simple
- a reduction in or lack of speech
- overeating or an increased liking for sweet foods.

It is important for the carer to realise that these changes are the result of a physical illness and that the individual is unable to modify their behaviour.

Vascular dementia

The brain cells need a good supply of blood so they can function properly. Blood is delivered to the brain via a network of blood vessels called the vascular system. If the vascular system within the brain becomes damaged and blood cannot reach the brain cells, the cells will die. This can lead to the development of vascular dementia.

There are a number of conditions that can cause damage to the brain's vascular system. These include high blood pressure, heart problems, high cholesterol and diabetes. Therefore, it is important that these conditions are diagnosed and treated as early as possible.

Vascular dementia affects people in different ways, depending on the cause. Some symptoms are similar to those of other types of dementia. However, people with vascular dementia are more likely to experience:

- problems concentrating and communicating
- depression
- symptoms of stroke, such as physical weakness or paralysis
- memory problem
- epileptic seizures
- periods of acute confusion
- hallucinations ie. seeing things that do not exist
- delusions ie. believing things that are not true
- walking about and getting lost
- physical or verbal aggression
- restlessness
- incontinence.

Certain factors can increase a person's risk of developing vascular dementia. These include:

- a medical history of stroke, high blood pressure, high cholesterol, diabetes, heart problems, or sleep apnoea (where breathing stops during sleep)
- a lack of physical activity, drinking more than recommended levels of alcohol, smoking, eating a fatty diet, or leaving conditions such as high blood pressure or diabetes untreated
- a family history of stroke or vascular dementia
- an Indian, Bangladeshi, Pakistani, Sri Lankan or African-Caribbean ethnic background.

Although vascular dementia cannot be reversed, it is possible to slow the progression of the disease by:

- treating underlying medical conditions such as high blood pressure, high cholesterol, diabetes or heart problems
- stopping smoking, taking regular exercise, eating healthily and drinking alcohol only in moderation
- offering physiotherapy, occupational therapy and speech therapy, to enable the person to regain any lost function or maximise residual function.

MAKING A DIAGNOSIS

A proper diagnosis of dementia is essential, in order to:

- rule out other conditions that may have symptoms similar to dementia, for example, depression
- rule out other possible causes of confusion, for example, the side effects of certain drugs
- access advice, information and support from social services and support groups
- allow the person with dementia to plan and make arrangements for the future.

As drugs for treating different conditions become available, it is becoming very important to identify which type of dementia a person has. For example, drugs are available to treat some people with Alzheimer's disease and also with DLB. However, the same drugs are ineffective in the treatment of Pick's disease, and may make this type of dementia worse.

Making a diagnosis of dementia can be difficult, particularly in the early stages, and a diagnosis may only be confirmed after death, at post mortem. Also, the time it takes to make a diagnosis can vary. For example, if brain scans and other investigations are required, it could be several weeks, depending on waiting lists.

If the person is in the early stages of dementia, several months of monitoring may be required before a specific diagnosis can be made. This delay can add to the anxiety and stress that individuals and their families are experiencing, particularly if changes in behaviour are left largely unexplained.

Assessment by the GP

The first person that the individual or family are likely to consult is the GP, who will often arrange a home visit. It is easier to assess and observe a person's behaviour in their own home, as it then becomes clearer exactly what the problems are. The GP will assess the person by undertaking:

- an analysis of the individual's family and job history, and social background to try and establish just what the symptoms are
- physical examinations and tests, for example, an examination of the nervous system and heart, and blood and urine tests, to identify other conditions that may be causing confusion
- tests of mental function and reasoning, for example, the GP may ask a series of questions designed to test thinking and memory.

At the end of the assessment, the GP may feel able to make a diagnosis, or they may wish for a specialist assessment to be undertaken.

Assessment by a specialist

A consultant will have more specialised knowledge and experience of dementia than the GP, and will have access to more specialised investigations, such as brain scans. The type of referral may depend on the age of the person, their symptoms and what is available in the individual's locality.

The main types of consultants are as follows:

- **neurologist:** he or she will specialise in disorders of the brain and nervous system; some neurologists have particular experience in diagnosing dementia
- **geriatrician:** he or she will specialise in the physical illnesses and disabilities associated with old age and in the care of older people
- **psychiatrist:** he or she will specialise in diagnosing and treating a wide range of mental health problems
- **psycho-geriatrician:** he or she is a psychiatrist who has specialised in the mental health problems of older people, including dementia.

The consultant works with a specialist team of other doctors who have undergone various stages of training in their particular speciality. The consultant also works with other health care professionals such as nurses, psychologists, occupational therapists and social workers and each of these bring their own unique knowledge, skills and advice to the dementia care team.

Specialist assessment

Assessment can take place in the home, in an outpatient department, in a day hospital or, as a hospital inpatient. The assessment will take several weeks and will include:

- **collection of background information;** the assessment will include time spent talking to the individual and to those who are close to them or have cared for them
- **physical examinations and tests,** for example, an examination of the nervous and cardiovascular system and some blood tests will be undertaken
- **behaviour assessment;** the individual will see a psychologist for a detailed assessment; time will be spent observing the individual's behaviour and their ability to cope
- **scans:** the person might be given a brain scan and some brain scans can identify conditions such as strokes, a brain tumour or a build-up of fluid inside the brain. Other types of scans show how the blood flows through the brain.

After the assessment, the consultant will send a report to the GP. The brain scans may show brain shrinkage, or areas of loss of brain function. The pattern of these changes will help the specialist to diagnose the exact cause of the dementia. Once a diagnosis is confirmed, the family GP will usually become responsible for the general health of the person with dementia. However, both the GP and the specialist will jointly prescribe any medication or supportive treatment for the dementia. The arrangements for ongoing care will depend upon the person's situation, where they live and what medication they have been prescribed.

The right to know

Some doctors have different views about what to tell their patients about their diagnosis. A person with dementia does have a right to be told their diagnosis, particularly if this enables them to put their personal affairs in order.

However, in some circumstances the GP or specialist may feel that they should only disclose the diagnosis if the patient asks, or seems to want to know; or the knowledge that they have dementia may be too much for the individual to cope with.

In some cases, it may be left to the relatives to decide whether to tell the individual that they have dementia. However, this will depend on the kind of relationship they have with the individual, what they feel the individual would want to know, and whether the individual has the capacity to understand.

CASE STUDY: JANET

'I decided to make an appointment to see my GP. Because I have difficulty finding words due to my Alzheimer's, I spent two hours writing down what I wanted to say. Also, I booked a double appointment because I knew I would be anxious and get tongue tied and it would take me a while to explain to the doctor what the problem was.

When I arrived at the doctor's surgery, I was told that my doctor had left and I would be seeing another one. She was very young and appeared to be nervous. I tried to explain what was wrong, but she made me even more nervous and the words just wouldn't come. She looked at her watch and said that I had been there quite a long time. I said that was why I had booked a double appointment.

She told me that it was probably all due to the fact that I was getting old. She seemed to be under a lot of stress. She didn't seem to have any understanding of my Alzheimer's and the problems I was having trying to explain to her what was wrong with me.

In the end, I left without her really understanding why I was there. She didn't help me at all. I've made another appointment to see a different doctor.'

Janet, *My doctor's appointment* (Alzheimer's Forum, 2007c)

CASE STUDY: BARRY

'Why is it that when we realise we have a problem with our memory and go to the doctor, some of them are reluctant or even disinclined to include us in the consultation diagnosis of dementia. They seem to think it's better we don't know and start talking over our heads to our partner and family.

I feel this is totally wrong, as adults even with dementia we have a right to know what our condition is. This can help us to overcome the first major stepping stone of accepting our dementia and rearranging our life accordingly. It can also help to motivate us to maintain some independence and fight in our daily life.

For many of us, we might have already guessed what our problem might be before we even go to the doctor, so please treat us with some respect and tell us the truth right to our face. We are not stupid people. Even though the brain might have become a bit slow and confused, it is still working and we can understand what's being said and as the patient/sufferer, we have the right to know the reality of our illness and be put on a course of medication ASAP to help our memory retention.

Unfortunately, therein lays another problem as with the present system of diagnosis, doctors can't always prescribe the best effective medication in the early stages. It's as if the powers that be see it as rearranging deckchairs on a sinking cruise ship. Demand to know the truth, as I did.'

Barry, *Tell us the truth* (Alzheimer's Forum, 2007a)

End of chapter quiz

1. According to the Alzheimer's Society (2009a) how many people in the UK suffer from dementia?

2. What are the most common types of dementia?

3. What is vascular dementia?

4. What is DLB?

5. Nightmares and hallucinations are symptoms most commonly associated with which type of dementia?

6. Which type of dementia is most commonly associated with memory loss?

7. Which type of dementia is most commonly associated with changes in personality and language difficulties?

8. Why is a brain scan of an individual undertaken?

9. What is a psycho-geriatrician?

10. What is meant by mild cognitive impairment (MCI)?

✍ My continuing professional development (CPD) log

Name of care worker ....

Name of manager/supervisor ....

Name of employer ....

Start date for dementia care training..

Expected date of completion ....

This is to confirm that .... [*name of care worker*] has satisfactorily completed...................... [*insert number*] of hours of study, and has achieved all of the following learning activities:

1. define the term 'dementia' and be able to differentiate this from other confusing states
2. outline the most common types and causes of dementia, for example, Alzheimer's disease, vascular disease, Lewy body and Pick's disease
3. describe the signs and symptoms of dementia and the physical, emotional and social effects this may have on the individual, for example, decline in memory, decline in reasoning and communication, changes in behaviour, loss of skills to carry out normal daily activities etc
4. explain how a diagnosis of dementia is made and the implications this has for the support and care of an individual.

Comments from care worker or supervisor, for example, outcomes of key learning activities or results of quiz.

Signed (care worker): .... Date:..............................

Signed (supervisor): .... Date:..............................

Chapter two

Supporting individuals with dementia

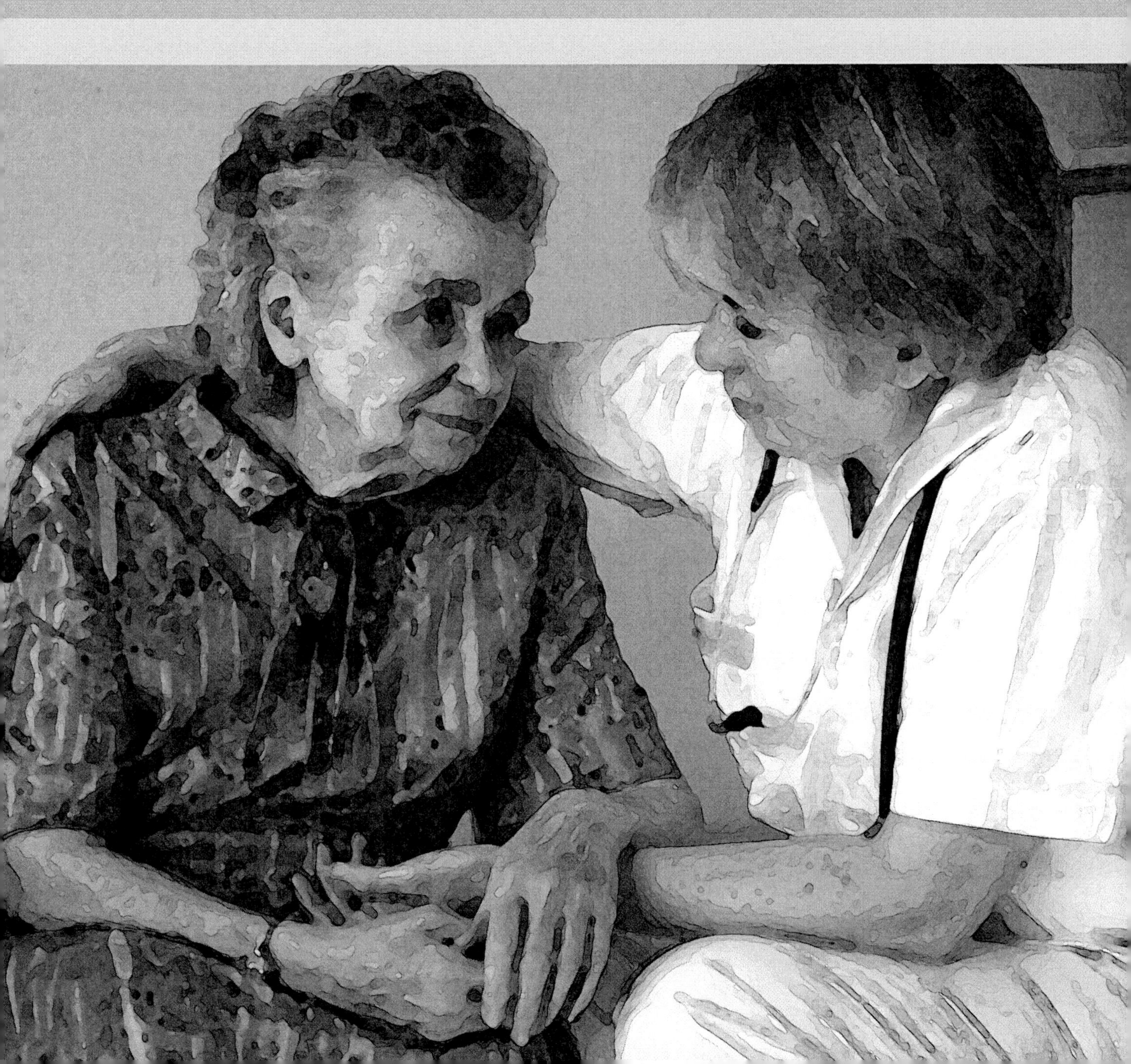

Chapter two

Supporting individuals with dementia

☺ Key learning activity

This activity will provide you with key background information before you read **chapter two**. Make a note of your answers and discuss these with a colleague or your supervisor before you commence with your reading.

Q. Go to http://www.alzheimers.org.uk/factsheet/507

- What might a person with dementia feel they are losing?
- What feelings might a person who is grieving experience?

AIMS OF THE CHAPTER

At the end of this part of the workbook, the learner will be able to:

1. outline the difference between medical and client-centred approaches to the care and support of individuals with dementia
2. highlight the feelings and issues that are commonly experienced by people with dementia, for example, social isolation, deprivation and loss
3. explain the need to support and work with family and friends of the individual
4. identify the services and support networks that are available to support the individual and his or her family.

APPROACHES TO DEMENTIA CARE

The medical model

One view of dementia is that it is a disease caused by deficits or impairments in brain function. These impairments are identified through a medical examination and various drugs can be prescribed to correct the deficit. For example, people with Alzheimer's have been shown to have a shortage of the chemical acetylcholine in their brains. This deficit can be corrected by the drugs donepezil, hydrochloride, rivastigmine and galantamine. However, the reality is that medical science knows very little about the cause or treatment of dementia and most forms still remain incurable (Alzheimer's Society, 2009a). There is, therefore a relatively negative and fearful view of dementia that exists amongst service users, which is characterised by physical and mental deterioration and a poor prognosis.

The social model

Another view of dementia is that impairments of brain function may become more obvious when the person finds themselves in an unhelpful or difficult situation. The emotional response of a person who is in a difficult or unhelpful situation is to become anxious, insecure, frustrated or embarrassed, and as a carer you can create helpful situations that may reduce a person's disability by understanding how they may be feeling and how these feelings may be affecting their behaviour. This is a more positive view of dementia as the impact of an individual's disability can be reduced if care staff are able to create an environment in which the individual can carry out their everyday activities, despite their disability. So, for example, planning and sequencing of tasks and activities leading to difficulty in dressing can be overcome by breaking down dressing activities into manageable stages (see Mrs Clark's story below).

CASE STUDY: MRS CLARK

Care staff noticed that Mrs Clark was getting into a muddle when dressing in the morning, for example, she was placing her undergarments on top of her dress. This meant that care staff had to redress Mrs Clark before she left her room for breakfast. Mrs Clark's key worker decided to place the clothes on the bed in the correct sequence and then prompt Mrs Clark to put these on in the correct order. Mrs Clark now has ample time to dress before she joins the other residents for breakfast and care staff report that she is less agitated in the mornings.

Also, judgement and safety awareness leading to difficulties while shopping can be reduced by undertaking a risk assessment and planning the safest route to the shops (see Mr Smith).

CASE STUDY: MR SMITH

Mr Smith's daughter noticed that when she walked with her father to the shop to collect his newspaper he was unable to judge the speed of traffic when he was crossing the road. She discussed this with care staff who recorded in Mr Smith's care plan that: (1) there is a risk to Mr Smith's safety when he is crossing the road; (2) he must always be accompanied by his daughter, or a carer when he collects his newspaper from the newsagent, and (3) the controlled pedestrian crossing should always be used when crossing the road with Mr Smith.

The above approaches are important as it helps us to recognise the positive attributes and the individual potential of a person with dementia, rather than emphasise their gradual mental or physical deterioration.

The importance of a positive caring relationship

The social approach towards dementia care shows how difficulties experienced by individuals are made worse by factors that are outside their control, such as negative relationships. A negative relationship can undermine an individual by taking away their independence and many carers (unthinkingly) can make matters worse by:

- doing something for a person when they are quite capable of doing it themselves
- talking about an individual as if they weren't there
- intimidating the person by using explicit or subtle threats
- taking away or limiting a person's choice
- ignoring a person's thoughts or feelings
- treating the person as an object.

☺ Activity: Other people's perceptions

Please read the following case study:

'I want to make my own decisions - people assume I can't.'

'People talk over my head and say, "What does she want?" "Does she like it?" "Does she take sugar?" They assume I can't speak for myself.'

'They say I don't look any different. How do they expect me to look?'

'People don't believe me because they say I am too young.'

'My teenage son made me a cup of coffee and I said, "Why did you do that?" and he said, "Because I didn't think you could do it".'

Other people's perceptions **(Alzheimer's Forum, 2005)**

Would you say that these perceptions are particularly helpful? What might they be based upon? Record your answers below and then discuss these with your supervisor.

Negative relationships and behaviours are often influenced by assumptions or stereotypes that carers have of people with dementia who are often seen as powerless and totally reliant on others for assisted care. As a consequence, the carer is often seen as an authority who takes control and leads rather than providing care in a collaborative way. Professor Tom Kitwood (1993) argued that negative relationships can undermine the person with dementia and make their mental state worse by de-skilling or undervaluing them. In order to avoid this, Professor Kitwood argued that dementia care should be based on a person-centred approach.

THE PERSON-CENTRED APPROACH

Fundamental to the person-centred approach is the need to recognise a person's:

- culture
- feelings
- individuality
- need for privacy
- need for respect.

Each of these will now be discussed in more detail.

Culture

When caring for a person with dementia, it is important that staff understand a person's cultural or religious background and any rules or customs that may apply. This will include the need to:

- use respectful forms of address
- identify how and what they prefer to eat
- establish religious observances, such as prayer or festivals
- identify clothing or jewellery that the person should or should not wear
- understand forms of touch or gesture that are considered disrespectful
- establish ways of undressing the person in order to maintain their dignity, including ways of dressing and how the person washes or uses the toilet.

Individuality

An individual's sense of who they are, is closely connected to the name they are called. Therefore, it is important that people address the person with dementia in a way that the person recognises and prefers. For example, some people may be happy to be called by their first name or nickname while others may prefer to be addressed as Mr or Mrs. Many people with dementia have a fragile sense of self-worth, therefore it is important that they are treated with courtesy. Care staff should:

- be kind and reassuring to the person without talking down to them
- never talk over the person's head as if they are not there
- include the person in conversations
- avoid criticising or making the person feel small
- try to imagine how they would like to be spoken to if you were in the same position
- listen carefully to the person even if they don't seem to be making much sense as they are trying to communicate how they feel.

Feelings

A person with dementia is likely, at times, to be sad or upset, particularly during the early stages of their illness when they may want to talk about any worries or concerns they have about their future. It is important that care staff:

- make time to offer support, rather than just 'jollying the person along'
- listen and show the person that they are there for them
- recognise how the person is feeling, for example, they may be able to judge this from the person's expression and/or body language
- always explain what they are doing, and why
- phrase questions carefully so that they only need a 'yes' or 'no' answer, as too much choice can often add to the person's confusion
- give the person every opportunity to make their own choices by informing and consulting with the person about matters that concern them.

Privacy

The person's right to privacy must be respected and care staff should always knock on the person's bedroom door before entering. If the person requires personal and intimate care such as washing or using the toilet, this must be done sensitively and the door to the bathroom or toilet should be kept closed.

Respect

When a person with dementia finds that their mental abilities are declining, they often feel vulnerable and are in need of reassurance and support. A person with dementia needs to feel respected and valued; in order to do this, carers need to:

- encourage the person to take pride in their appearance, and compliment them on how they look
- do things with the person, rather than for them, to help them retain their independence
- avoid situations in which the person is likely to fail, as this can be humiliating
- look for tasks and activities that the individual can still manage and enjoy
- break activities down into small steps so that they feel a sense of achievement, even if they can only manage part of a task
- let individuals do things at their own pace and in their own way
- give plenty of praise and encouragement.

COPING WITH LOSS AND CHANGE

CASE STUDY

'Despite what other people might say, I can observe changes within my own personality. No longer am I the self-confident person I used to be. Now I feel very insecure and withdrawn.'

'Simple jobs around the house, like changing electrical plugs, decorating, or even to open a tin of canned food, has become more like a major obstacle in life.'

'I always used to be a very calm placid person with logical thinking, but now I can very quickly lose all sense of reasoning to the point of becoming verbally agressive, which must confuse my family as it's a complete reverse to my pre-illness nature.'

'My communication skills are rapidly diminishing and to write a letter or try to solve any type of family problem is now almost beyond my capabilities without help.'

'When I'm confronted by other people talking about my illness, I notice that I become far more agitated and shaky as I try to explain about my Alzheimer's. It's as if my subconscious is trying to emphasise the problem.'

'What I notice is that my ability to control money and any household financial matters is now beyond me, so I must leave it all to my wife as it all confuses me.'

What changes I notice in myself as a result of the illness **(Alzheimer's Forum, 2008a)**

As you can see from the above case study, people with dementia have to cope with many lifestyle changes and these are often associated with loss, which can be emotional, physical or social. It has been shown that individuals with dementia who suffer loss, or who are grieving due to the effects of change, often experience similar stages of grief. These stages include:

- **denial** – people who know they are losing their mental abilities will often deny this by making up stories to cover their memory loss; this is known as *confabulation*
- **anger** – people with dementia may feel as if they have lost control of their lives and may become resentful
- **rationalisation** – people with dementia may find it more difficult to make sense of their situation as they will have lost their ability to sequence their thoughts and actions and to solve problems
- **acceptance** – the person begins to adapt and make changes to compensate for their loss.

As a consequence, people with dementia may feel a range of emotions such as anger, anxiety and depression. They may exhibit behaviours such as angry outbursts, or extreme laughter and may become upset or suspicious because they misunderstand things they overhear. Each of these issues are now discussed in more detail.

Anger

Anger often arises as a response to feeling frightened, frustrated, or humiliated, for example, being surrounded by strangers can be frightening for individuals with dementia. Similarily, being surrounded by lots of activity and noise can be distracting or upsetting. Some people with dementia may also get frustrated when they can't successfully perform a task. In order to minimise the effects of frustration, the care worker should try breaking down complex tasks into manageable steps and each step should be achieved before further instructions are given. Also, tasks should be set that will allow the person to have a say in what is happening. Finally, if all else fails, it is important to give the person time and space in order that they may calm down.

Depression

Depression is a common experience for individuals with dementia. The feeling of social isolation and loss of control that comes with the progression of dementia may contribute to depression. It can sometimes be difficult for care workers to distinguish depression from dementia since some of the symptoms are the same, such as apathy, changes in mood, memory loss, trouble sleeping, delusions, agitation and anxiety. However, symptoms usually associated with other forms of depression, such as guilt, suicidal thoughts and low-self esteem are not as common. If a care worker is concerned about a particular service user, they should talk to the doctor to find out if medical treatment or counselling is needed. Also, it is important to keep the person active and to keep them socially involved.

Anxiety

New places and faces can be unsettling for a person with dementia, especially when familiar places and faces have been forgotten. Some people respond to anxiety by pacing, insomnia, and restlessness while others may choose to cling to familiar objects or individuals. Care workers should reassure the individual and remind them how much they care. Additionally, it is helpful to come up with activities that the person can focus on instead of worrying.

Finally, it is important for the care worker to realise that although they may not be able to control the emotions of service users, they can control their own reactions to them and turn a potentially negative situation into a more positive one. This can be done by following these three steps for dealing with emotional outbursts:

- reassure
- respond
- refocus.

These steps are now discussed in more detail.

Reassure and let the person know that you are there by saying 'I'm here, I will help you'. A simple touch can calm an upset person. However, touch may also further trigger emotions for someone who is already aggravated.

Respond to the emotional content; regardless of whether the person is reacting to something that you consider serious or trivial, it is important for you to recognise and respect the person's feelings, for example, you might say, *'It sounds like you are upset that your son will be late'*.

Refocus the person's attention. Rather than allowing the person to dwell on a subject that is difficult or painful, try to redirect the conversation. The best way to redirect a conversation is to listen and to follow the flow of the conversation, for example, *'Being on time must be very important to you. You were always very considerate like that. But when your son gets here, I'm sure he will stay a little longer with you?'*

☺ Activity: My dad

Please read the following case study:

'My dad used to be reserved when he got frustrated or angry. After he started to show signs of early dementia, he threw a golf club in anger during a golf game after taking a bad shot. We were shocked because he had never acted like that before. Now that I care for him, he'll sometimes throw food or a fork at me if he's angry. It's so strange because it doesn't seem like him. I've found that he gets angry less often when I plan ahead to make things easier for him where he needs help, like cutting his meat up before he gets to the dinner table; and when he does get angry, I distract him from whatever upsets him and talk soothingly. He usually calms down fairly quickly.'

(Dementia Care Central, 2009)

What strategies did the daughter use to minimise her father's anger? List your answers below and then discuss them with your supervisor.

☺ Activity: Barry's 10 tips for staying positive

Please read the following case study:

'The first and most important stepping stone is to accept you have a type of dementia and that it's not going to go away. Now be positive in mind.

Contact your nearest Alzheimer's Society branch, become involved with their activities as much as you can, communicate with Alzheimer's Forum and share your feelings and thoughts.

Talk openly and freely about your dementia. Don't try to hide it or keep it a secret from family, friends or other people. It's just an illness – not a stigma.

Accept you must make adjustments to your daily life and the way you do things, write yourself a list of goals, objectives and coping strategies as this can be different for all of us, keep the list where you can see it all the time as a reminder.

Stay as active as possible, look for easier ways of doing past interests or even try doing something new, as even with dementia, we can still learn new skills, like using a computer.

Don't say 'I can't do that any more', say 'Yes, I still can' but just take your time, don't push yourself too hard – pace yourself.

Accept you will have good days and bad days. Openly discuss the bad days with your partner and how to cope with them together.

Make friends with a fellow sufferer no matter how far apart you might live. Communicate with each other by e-mail or recorded talks, it's better than telephoning and helps to keep the brain actively thinking.

Keep a daily diary or computer diary of your condition and activities. Using the computer to do this is good brain stimulation and can help eye-to-hand co-ordination.

Give thanks to God each day for still having life and remember there is always someone in this world worse off than we are: so live life to the full.'

(Alzheimer's Forum, 2007b)

At what stage of the grieving process would you say Barry was at? Justify and record your answer below. Discuss your answer with your supervisor.

WORKING WITH FRIENDS AND FAMILY

During the early stages of dementia

When a person develops dementia, their partner, spouse, family member or a friend are also likely to experience feelings of grief and bereavement as the person's illness progresses. For example, they might come to terms with one stage of the person's illness only to find that the person's behaviour alters, or their abilities decline further, and then their grieving may start all over again.

A sense of loss is one of the most powerful feelings that people experience when someone close to them develops dementia and depending on their relationship with the person, and their individual circumstances, they may grieve for the loss of the person they once knew; the future they had planned together; the relationship they once shared; their own freedom to work or to pursue other activities; a lifestyle that they once took for granted; their companionship.

In the early stages of a person's dementia, the spouse or partner's mood may swing between despair and optimism as they believe that a cure might be found. The partner may also deny that anything is wrong with the person and may try to suppress their feelings. Later, when they have accepted the situation, the spouse or family member may find that there are periods when they can cope well and make the best of things. However, they may also feel overwhelmed by sadness or anger, or may simply feel numb.

People who have cared for someone with dementia often feel resentful for the restrictions that have been placed on their own life. They may feel guilty that that they have placed a loved one into a care home and may feel unhappy that things have not turned out as they would have hoped. Some people are shocked to find that they sometimes wish that their spouse was dead.

Feelings like these are a normal part of grieving and it is important for the care worker to realise that the spouse or partner may be under a great deal of stress, and may need emotional support for themselves.

As a care worker you should encourage the partner or spouse to:

- talk about their feelings
- relieve tension, for example, through crying
- maintain contact with friends
- to see their GP if they are feeling low or anxious, or if they are very tired and unable to sleep
- consider their own need, for example, taking regular breaks from visiting can keep them in touch with the outside world and raise their spirit
- put aside some time to themselves each day, for example, relaxing with a cup of tea or having a good chat on the phone will often help them to recharge their batteries.

During the final stages of dementia

In the final stages of dementia, the service user may be unable to recognise their spouse or partner. This can be very painful for close relatives as although their relationship is almost at an end, they are unable to grieve fully because the person is still alive. It might be helpful if the carer encourages the spouse or partner to hold the person's hand or sit with their arm around them. It is also important for the carer to reassure the spouse that they have done all they can to make their partner comfortable.

Some people find that they grieve so much during the course of their loved one's illness that they have no strong feelings left when the person dies. Others may experience a range of overwhelming reactions and emotions. These may include:

- numbness
- an inability to accept the situation
- shock and pain
- relief, both for their spouse or partner and themselves
- anger and resentment
- sadness and feelings of isolation.

Those who have been coping with a partner's illness for some time will be left with a huge space to fill when their partner dies, and will often find it difficult to find a meaning, purpose or structure to their lives. It is important that the carer understands that grieving family members:

- are often shocked or vulnerable and may not be able to make any rationale decisions about their lives
- may show that they are coping but underneath they are often feeling sad or upset
- should stay in touch with their GP as they are likely to be more vulnerable to physical illness, anxiety or depression following their bereavement.

It is important that carers dignify and pay respect to dying individuals, their bereaved family and friends. They can do this by:

- placing a favourite possession of the deceased on the trolley and allow the body to be removed through the front door of the home
- ensure that the news of a service user's death is communicated sensitively to staff and residents; some homes pin a photograph on the notice board, place a flower in a vase or light a candle
- provide opportunities for the home to stop for a moment of quiet to respect the significance of the resident's life and death
- provide a place for staff to talk with relatives and residents about their feelings and to exchange thoughts about the person who has died

- facilitate the sharing of memories of the deceased, for example, by providing a book of remembrance
- allow residents and staff personal acts of commemoration, such as attending the funeral or planting a flower in the care home garden.

(Help the Aged, 2008)

SERVICES AND SUPPORT NETWORKS

As we have already discussed, a person with dementia will need an increasing amount of support as their condition progresses and their local authority has a duty to carry out an assessment in order to decide which services could be arranged to support them.

The services arranged by local authorities are known as 'community care services'. They vary from area to area, but may include:

- home care services
- equipment and adaptations
- day care services
- short breaks (respite) in a care home or a person's own home
- residential care.

The financial situation of the person with dementia is taken into account, and they may be asked to contribute towards the cost of these services.

Local authorities also provide services for informal carers, for example, family members who are entitled to a local authority assessment of their needs regarding the care they provide.

Some services, such as community nursing, are arranged through the NHS. The person's GP or hospital consultant will arrange these.

Voluntary organisations provide services such as information, helplines, support groups, lunch clubs and home care schemes. The local Alzheimer's Society branch, Citizens Advice Bureau or Age Concern can provide these details.

Carers should be aware of the different types of organisations that might assist and support service users and families. Some of these are listed below, together with an outline of their function:

USEFUL ORGANISATIONS

Age Concern England
Freepost SWB 30375
Ashburton
Devon TQ13 7ZZ

T: 0800 009 966 (free helpline everyday 8am–7am)
E: use the enquiry form on the website (see below)
W: http://www.ace.org.uk/

Provides advice and information for older people in England.

Age Concern Cymru
Ty John Pathy
13–14 Neptune Court
Vanguard Way
Cardiff CF24 5PJ
T: 02920 413 555
E: enquiries@accymru.org.uk
W: http://www.accymru.org.uk/

Provides advice and information for older people in Wales.

Alzheimer's Society
Devon House
58 St Katharine's Way
London E1W 1JX
T: 0207 423 3500
0845 300 0336 (helpline open 8.30am–6.30pm weekdays)
E: info@alzheimers.org.uk (general information)
helpline@alzheimers.org.uk (helpline)
W: alzheimers.org.uk

The UK's leading care and research charity for people with dementia and those who care for them. The helpline provides information, support, guidance and referrals to other appropriate organisations.

Benefit Enquiry Line (BEL)
Red Rose House
Lancaster Road
Preston
Lancashire PR1 1HB
T: 0800 882 200
(free helpline open 8.30am–6.30pm weekdays and 9am–1pm Saturdays)
0800 243 544 (textphone)
E: BEL-Customer-Services@dwp.gsi.gov.uk
W: www.direct.gov.uk/disability-money

National, free telephone advice and information service on benefits for people with disabilities, their carers and representatives. Note that advisers can send out forms and give advice but they have no access to personal records.

Carers UK
20 Great Dover Street
London SE1 4LX
T: 0808 808 7777 (free carers' line, Wednesday and Thursday 10am–12pm and 2pm–4pm)
E: info@ukcarers.org
W: http://www.carersuk.org/

Provides information and advice to carers about their rights and how to access support.

Counsel and Care
Twyman House
16 Bonny Street
London NW1 9PG
T: 0845 300 7585 (advice line, weekdays 10am–4pm except Wednesdays 10am–1pm)
E: advice@counselandcare.org.uk
W: http://www.counselandcare.org.uk/

Provides advice, information and financial support for older people, their families and carers.

Department for Work and Pensions
For details of your local office, go to www.dwp.gov.uk/localoffice
For details of various helplines, go to www.dwp.gov.uk/contact/contact_atoz.asp
T: 08457 123 456
E: use the enquiry form on the website (see below)
W: http://www.dwp.gov.uk/

The government department responsible for employment and social security. Its website gives details of the various benefits and how to claim them, and has claim forms available to download.

Help the Aged (England)
207–221 Pentonville Road
London N1 9UZ
T: 020 7278 1114
0808 800 6565 (senior line freephone, weekdays 9am–4pm)
E: info@helptheaged.org.uk
W: http://www.helptheaged.org.uk/

Provides advice and reliable information for older people and their carers.

Help the Aged (Wales)
12 Cathedral Road
Cardiff CF11 9LJ
T: 02920 346 550
E: infocymru@helptheaged.org.uk
W: http://www.helptheaged.org.uk/

Office of the Public Guardian (OPG)
Archway Tower
2 Junction Road
London N19 5SZ
T: 0845 330 2900 (customer services, 9am–5pm weekdays)
E: customerservices@publicguardian.gsi.gov.uk
W: http://www.publicguardian.gov.uk/

Supports and promotes decision-making for those who lack capacity or would like to plan for their future, within the framework of the Mental Capacity Act (2005). Provides free booklets on enduring power of attorney and receivership. The court of protection is at the same address.

End of chapter quiz

1. Complete the following sentence: 'Fundamental to the person-centred approach is the need to recognise a person's: culture, ... '

2. What are the four stages of grief?

3. What are the three steps for dealing with an emotional outburst?

4. List three community care services that are available to service users with dementia.

5. Who are the Alzheimer's Society and what do they do?

✍ My continuing professional development (CPD) log

Name of care worker ....

Name of manager/supervisor ....

Name of employer ....

Start date for dementia care training..

Expected date of completion ....

This is to confirm that .... [*name of care worker*] has satisfactorily completed...................... [*insert number*] of hours of study, and has achieved all of the following learning activities:

1. outline the difference between medical and client-centred approaches to the care and support of individuals with dementia
2. highlight the feelings and issues that are commonly experienced by people with dementia, for example, social isolation, deprivation and loss
3. explain the need to support and work with family and friends of the individual
4. identify the services and support networks that are available to support the individual and his or her family.

Comments from care worker or supervisor, for example, outcomes of key learning activities or results of quiz.

Signed (care worker): .... Date:..............................

Signed (supervisor): .... Date:..............................

Chapter three

Caring for the person with dementia

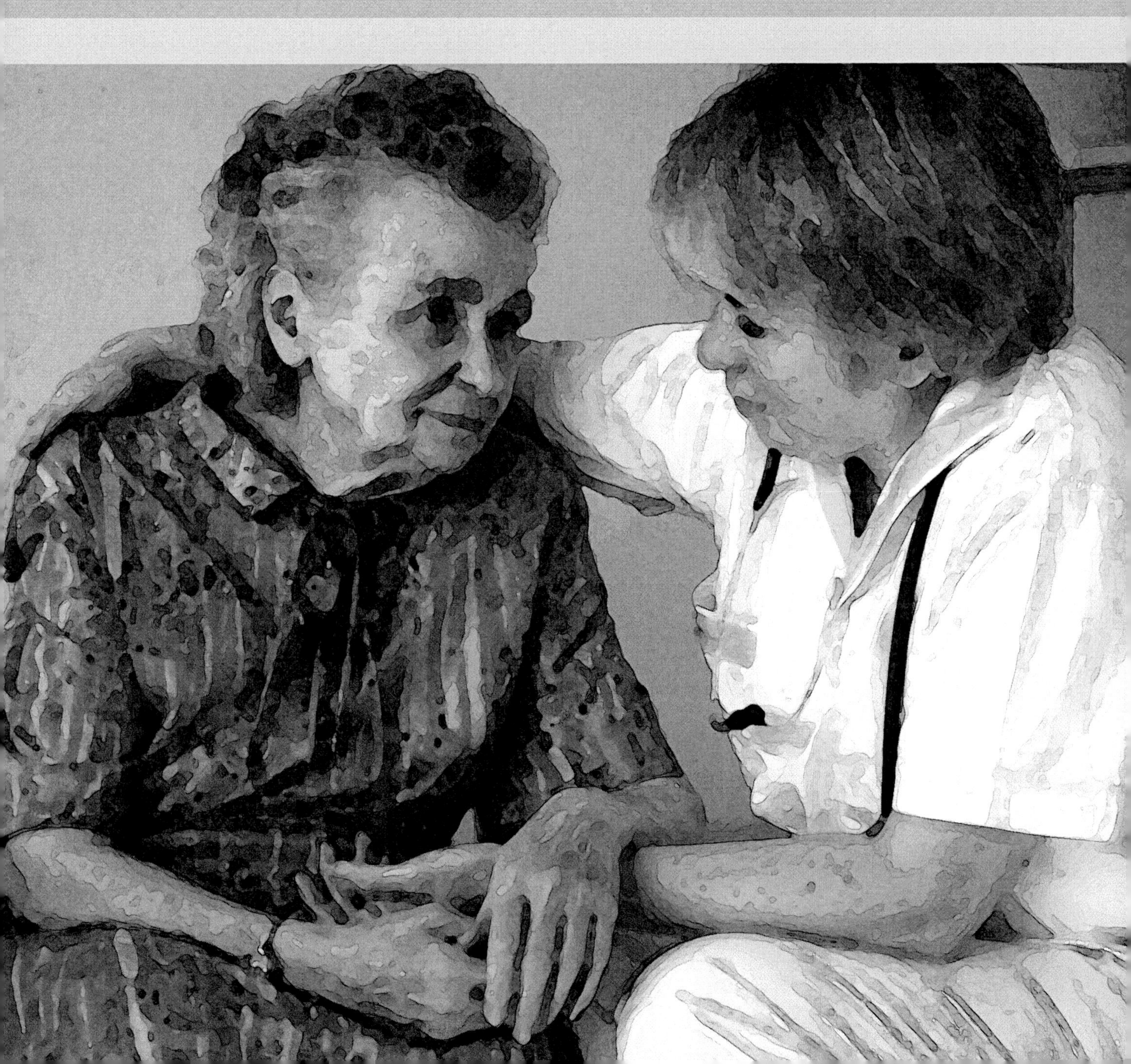

Chapter three

Caring for the person with dementia

☺ Key learning activity

This activity will provide you with key background information before you set about completing the next chapter. Make a note of your answers and discuss these with a colleague or your supervisor before you commence with your reading.

Q. Go to http://www.alzheimers.org.uk/factsheet/501

- Why might people with dementia feel compelled to walk about?
- How might the risks associated with this activity be minimised?

AIMS OF THE CHAPTER

At the end of this part of the workbook, the learner will be able to:

- discuss the need for positive and effective communications with the individual with dementia, for example, listening; responding; encouraging
- describe the importance of maintaining the health, safety and well-being of the individual with dementia, for example, mobility; nutrition; personal care etc
- outline activities, therapies and medication that may be used to help individuals with dementia, for example, prescribed and alternative or complimentary therapies
- outline the principles of safeguarding vulnerable people.

ENSURING POSITIVE AND EFFECTIVE COMMUNICATION

What changes I notice in myself as a result of the illness?

'My communication skills are rapidly diminishing and to write a letter or try to solve any type of family problem is now almost beyond my capabilities without help.'

(Alzheimer's Forum, 2008a)

Dementia can gradually reduce a person's ability to communicate effectively. People with dementia have difficulty expressing thoughts and emotions, they also have trouble understanding what others say. The person with dementia may experience changes in communication such as:

- difficulty finding the right words
- inventing new words to describe familiar objects

- easily lose their train of thought
- difficulty organising and sequencing words
- frequent use of swear words
- speaking less often or becoming mute
- more often relying on gestures instead of speaking.

Communications can be improved if you:

- always approach the person from the front and introduce yourself
- call the person by their name as it will orientate the person and get their attention
- let the person know you are listening and are trying to understand what is being said
- maintain eye contact as this shows the person that you care about what is being said
- focus on the feelings behind the words rather than content of the sentence
- avoid criticising, correcting or arguing with the individual
- ask the person to point or gesture if you don't understand what is being said
- talk slowly and clearly, using simple words and sentences
- use simple rather than complicated questions and ask questions one at a time
- allow the person extra time to think about your question before they give an answer
- give responses in a clear and concise way.

Responding to aggression

What changes I notice in myself as a result of the illness?

'I always used to be a very calm placid person with logical thinking, but now I can very quickly lose all sense of reasoning to the point of becoming verbally aggressive, which must confuse my family as it's a complete reverse to my pre-illness nature.'

(Alzheimer's Forum, 2008a)

A person with dementia may be verbally aggressive (abusive and shouting) or physically aggressive (hitting, pushing). These types of behaviour can occur suddenly, with no apparent reason, or can result from a frustrating situation. Whatever the reason, your job as a care worker is to try and understand what is causing the person to become angry or upset so that their anger can be minimised. Aggression can be caused by many factors including:

1. physical discomfort
2. environmental factors
3. poor communication.

Each of these causes are now considered in more detail.

1. Physical discomfort

- Is the person tired due to lack of rest or sleep?
- Are there any side effects from their medication?
- Is the person experiencing pain or other physical symptoms such as a full bladder?

2. Environmental factors

- Is the person upset by loud noises, a busy environment, or large crowds?
- Does the person feel lost or disorientated?

3. Poor communication

- Are you asking too may questions or giving too many explanations at once?
- Are your explanations and instructions simple and easy to understand?
- Is the person picking up on your own anxiety, stress, or irritability?
- Are you being judgemental or critical of the person?

How to respond.

- Assess the level of danger for yourself and the person with dementia, for example, you can often avoid harm by simply stepping back and standing away from the person. Or, if the person is attempting to leave the home, be more assertive.
- Try to identify the cause; think about what happened just before the aggressive outburst. What might have triggered the behaviour?
- Concentrate on the person's emotions, rather than the facts ie. look for the feelings behind the words.
- Don't get angry or upset; the person isn't necessarily angry with you. Be positive. Speak slowly and in a soft tone.
- Alter the person's surroundings to avoid similar situations, for example, try to introduce a relaxing activity such as music, massage or exercise to help soothe the problem.
- Shift the focus to another activity. The immediate situation or activity may have unintentionally caused the aggressive response. Try something different.
- Unless the situation is serious, avoid physically holding or restraining the person. He or she may become more agitated and the restraint may cause personal injury.

It is important to record incidents of aggression in the person's care plan, and possibly in an incident report depending on local policy. The information gained during the reporting process will:

- assist in determining the underlying cause
- ensure consistency of care across the care team

- assist in identifying the training needs of care staff
- ensure that an open and transparent approach towards the management of aggression is undertaken.

Dealing with confusion

Laughing at dementia and why not?

Just a line to say I'm living
That I'm not among the dead
Though I'm getting more forgetful
And mixed up in the head.
I have got used to my arthritis,
To my dentures I'm resigned,
I can cope with my bifocals,
But ye gods, I miss my mind.
Oft times I can't remember
When I'm standing by the stairs
If I'm going up for something
Or have I just come down from there,
And before the fridge so often
My mind is full of doubt,
Now did I put some food away
Or have I come to get some out,
And if it's not my turn to write
I hope you won't get sore
I might have written twice today and
Once the day before.
Just remember I love you
But now it's time to post this,
So cheerio, my dear
I stand before the post box now
And boy is my face red.

Bill (Alzheimer's Forum, 2008c)

The person with dementia will often not recognise familiar people, places or objects. He or she may call family members by different names or become confused about where their home is. They may also forget the purpose of common objects, such as a knife or a fork. These situations can be extremely stressful for care staff and for families, and require both patience and understanding from every member of the care team.

How to respond.

- Stay calm and respond with a brief explanation; don't overwhelm the person with lengthy ideas. Instead, clarify with a simple instruction.
- Use photographs and other memorabilia to remind the person of family relationships and places.

- Offer corrections as suggestions rather than fact, for example, try: *'I thought it was a knife'* or *'I think she is your daughter Elsie'*. Your tone should be calm and non-judgemental.
- Try not to take it personally as your support and understanding will be appreciated.

Dealing with hallucinations

A hallucination is a false perception of objects or events involving the senses. When individuals hallucinate, they see, hear, smell, taste or feel something that isn't there. The person may see the face of a family member reflected in a mirror, or may hear people talking. If the hallucination isn't causing any problems for staff, the person or their family, it can be ignored. However, if the hallucinations are continuous and the person's daily living is being disrupted, it is important to establish what the cause might be. In which case, a referral to the GP might be appropriate.

How to respond.

- Respond in a calm, supportive manner and offer reassurance. A gentle tap touch of the arm or on shoulder may turn the person's attention towards you. Don't argue with the person about what he or she sees.
- Look for the feelings behind the behaviour. You could say calmly, *'It sounds as if you're anxious'* or *'I know this is worrying you'*.
- Alter the environment, for example, check for noises that might be misinterpreted, such as a loud television. Check for lighting that casts reflections or distortions on the surfaces of floors. Cover mirrors if the person is frightened by their own reflection.
- Use distractions, for example, you could suggest that you take a walk or sit in another room. Frightening hallucinations will often subside in well-lit areas where other people are present. Try to turn the person's attention to music, conversation or activities you enjoy together.

Dealing with repetitive behaviour

The person with dementia will often do or say something over and over again, for example, pace up and down; repeatedly rearrange their belongings; or repeat a question such as *'Why am I here?'* or *'What is this place?'*. In most cases, he or she is probably looking for reassurance and some degree of comfort and security; and because these actions are rarely harmful it is often better to accept the persons behaviour and find ways of working with it.

How to respond.

- Look for a reason behind their behaviour and try to find out if there is a specific cause for the repetition.
- Focus on the emotion, rather than reacting to what the person is doing, think about how he or she is feeling.

- Stay calm and be patient. Reassure the person with a calm voice and gentle touch.
- Provide an answer. Try and give the person the answer that he or she is looking for, even if you have to repeat it several times.
- Engage the person in an activity. The individual may simply be bored and need something to do.
- If the person asks the same questions over and over again, offer reminders by using notes, clocks, or calendars.

Dealing with night-time restlessness

How do you cope with sleepless nights?

'Insomnia is a very big problem for me as almost every night I wake up at 2–3am but the strange thing is that I actually feel very fresh, alert and ready to work again. In fact, it's almost my best time of the day.'

'My problem is almost the reverse. I don't seem able to motivate myself and so I sleep a lot during the day. I sleep too much during the day.'

'Even though I have sleeping tablets, I still wake up very early and get dressed ready for the day. My wife realises it's all part of my illness, but to be on the safe side she always removes the front and back door keys so I can't get outside the house and maybe go wandering.'

'Waking up in the early hours can be an annoying problem, but even so I try to remember to be as quiet as I can so as not to disturb my wife as she needs her rest more than I do, as she is the one that must cope with me through the rest of the day as my sleepless nights can lead to irritability later in the day.'

(Alzheimer's Forum, 2008b)

People with dementia will, at some point, experience periods of increased confusion, anxiety, agitation and disorientation at night. This often begins at dusk and continues throughout the night. This may be caused by the following factors:

- less need for sleep, which is common among older adults
- an upset in the 'internal body clock' causing a mix-up between day and night
- reduced lighting and increased shadows
- disorientation due to an inability to separate dreams from reality when sleeping.

Care workers may reduce night-time sleeplessness by:

- reviewing any medication that the person might be taking with the GP, as this might be making them feel drowsy and sleepy during the day
- planning a more active day ie. a person who sleeps most of the day is likely to be awake at night

- reducing caffeine intake before bedtime
- serving dinner early and offering only a light meal or snack before bedtime
- allowing the person to sleep in a favourite chair or wherever it's most comfortable
- keep the person's room partially lit to reduce any agitation that may occur in dark or unfamiliar surroundings.

Safety is an important aspect if people are restless and wandering at night. Access to rooms or floor levels should be restricted by closing and locking doors. Motion detectors can be used to alert staff when a person is wandering, or to light dark places. Physical symptoms such as pain, constipation, bladder or incontinence problems could be making it difficult for the person to sleep. If these are suspected, the GP should be informed. Once the person is awake, carers should approach the person in a calm manner and:

- find out if there is something he or she needs, for example, a painkiller or a drink?
- avoid arguing or asking for explanations
- gently remind him or her that it is night-time
- offer reassurance that everything is all right and everyone is safe.

Responding to suspicious behaviour

Memory loss and confusion will cause the person with dementia to interpret things differently. Individuals may become suspicious of those around them. They may accuse partners or spouses of infidelity or other improper behaviour. They may accuse others of theft; they may also misinterpret what they hear.

How to respond.

- Try not to take any comments personally.
- Listen to what the person is saying then reassure them and let them know you care.
- Allow the person to express their concerns and accept his or her opinions.
- Don't argue with the person.
- Offer a simple explanation. Share your thoughts with the individual, but keep it simple.
- Distract the individual by engaging them in an activity, for example, ask for help with a simple chore.
- If the person is searching for a specific everyday item, for example, a newspaper or a cup, have several available for them to use.

Dealing with unpredictable behaviour

People with dementia can act in different and unpredictable ways but it is important to remember that the person is not acting this way deliberately. Whatever the behaviour, it is important for the carer to try to identify the cause and a possible solution. For example, individuals with dementia may forget that they are married and begin to flirt or make inappropriate advances towards others. Or they may take clothes off at inappropriate times and in unusual settings. For example, a woman may remove a blouse or skirt simply because it is too tight or uncomfortable. When there is unusual or inappropriate behaviour, try to distract the person with another activity, or lead him or her into a private place. Avoid getting angry or laughing at the person. Finally, it is important to record what has happened in the person's care plan as this will ensure consistency of information and approach across the care team.

MAINTAINING THE HEALTH, SAFETY AND WELL-BEING OF SERVICE USERS

Minimising risks and dangers

The person with dementia may be at risk if he or she can reach certain areas of the home or outdoors. As a care worker, you can ensure:

- potentially hazardous areas are locked or disguised; cover doors and locks with a painted mural or cloth; use swinging or folding doors to hide entrances to the kitchen or stairwell
- locks are installed out of sight; place deadbolts either high or low on exterior doors to make it difficult for the person to wander out of the house
- that there are two-way locks in bathrooms or bedrooms so the person cannot get locked inside
- that there are child-proof locks and door knob covers to limit access to places where knives, appliances and poisonous cleaning fluids are stored.

Most accidents occur during daily activities such as eating, bathing and using the bathroom. Therefore, as a care worker you should:

- check the temperature of water and food because the person may not know the difference between hot and cold
- use walk-in showers and grab bars in the shower or bath and next to the toilet, to allow the person to move around independently and safely
- add textured stickers to slippery surfaces; apply adhesives to keep throw rugs and carpeting in place – or remove rugs completely from ensuite rooms
- supervise the person while taking medication; ensure medicine trolleys, cabinets and cupboards containing prescription and over-the-counter drugs are locked.

Even the most basic appliance or household object can become dangerous for the person with dementia, and as a care worker you may need to:

- remove electrical appliances from the bathroom, such as electric razors or hair dryers, to reduce the risk of electrical shock
- put away dangerous kitchen appliances and utensils like mixers and knives

- put away any power tools or ladders that may have been left unattended by handymen or cleaners
- supervise smoking and the use of alcohol
- keep walking areas clear by removing magazine racks, coffee tables and floor lamps.

A person with dementia may not be able to distinguish colours or understand what is being seen because of changes in his or her vision. As a care worker you can:

- reduce the glare and any bright light by removing mirrors from walls and glass tops from cabinets; bright sunlight can be reduced by covering windows with blinds or shades or net curtains
- ensure that there is an even level of lighting within the home by adding extra lighting in outside landings, areas between rooms, stairways and bathrooms; changes in levels of light can disorientate a person with dementia
- use contrasting coloured carpets in front of doors or steps to help the individual anticipate staircases and room entrances
- use night lights in bedrooms and bathrooms to prevent accidents and reduce disorientation.

Caring for a person who wanders

Simple as ABC

It's easy as A B C going to the shops
but I get scared inside of me
and I begin to hop.

I went to the butcher's to get some chops for tea
and it was very hard
to find some peace inside of me.

I looked to the left and looked to the right
and all that I could see
was people marching by me
and then I saw a bee.

How do you do and how are you?
said a lady to my face.
I did not recognise her
she wore such lovely lace.

Keith (Alzheimer's Forum, 2007d)

It is common for a person with dementia to wander and become lost. It is estimated by the Alzheimer's Society that over 60% of those with dementia will wander at some point. Wandering can be potentially dangerous or even life threatening to the person with dementia.

Often, people with dementia who wander will have some purpose or goal in mind, for example, they may be searching for someone or something that is lost, or trying to undertake an activity relating to a previous job. A person may be considered to be at risk from wandering if he or she:

- regularly returns from walks later than usual
- repeatedly attempts to undertake former roles and responsibilities, for example, trying to go to work
- is frequently asking to 'go home' or attempting to leave the care home
- is continuously restless, pacing up and down or is making repetitive movements
- has trouble finding everyday places like the bathroom, bedroom, dining room or lounge
- repeatedly checks the whereabouts of people they know, for example, 'Where is my daughter now?'
- acts as if they are participating in a hobby or chore, but nothing really gets done, for example, constantly moving objects around without using them
- appears lost in an unfamiliar environment.

Wandering can be caused by:

- side effects of medication
- confusion related to time
- restlessness and agitation
- stress or anxiety
- inability to recognise familiar people, places and objects
- fear arising from the misinterpretation of sights and sounds
- a need to fulfil former roles and responsibilities, such as going to work or looking after a child.

Wandering can be reduced by:

- encouraging physical activity and exercise to reduce anxiety, agitation and restlessness
- ensuring that all basic needs are met, for example, toileting, nutrition, thirst
- involving the person in daily activities, such as folding laundry or preparing dinner
- redirecting restless behaviour

- reassuring the person if they feel abandoned or disorientation
- placing a mirror near doorways ie. their own reflection may stop them from going through the door.

Personal hygiene and appearance

Bathing a person with dementia can be a particularly difficult activity. It is such an intimate experience and people with dementia often perceive it as unpleasant or threatening. As a consequence, they may act in disruptive ways, like screaming, resisting or hitting. This type of behaviour often happens because the person doesn't remember what bathing is for, or doesn't tolerate a lack of modesty, or being cold or other minor discomforts. In order to avoid this behaviour, the care worker should encourage the person to do as much as possible for themselves, but be ready to assist when needed – particularly if safety becomes an issue. The care worker should:

1. Make an initial risk assessment of the person's ability to:

- recognise any potential danger
- find the bathroom
- keep their balance
- sense water temperature
- remember steps in the bathing process
- use different bathing products, for example, soap, shampoo, washcloth, etc.

The outcomes of this risk assessment should be recorded in the person's care plan.

2. Prepare the bathroom in advance.

- Gather bathing supplies such as towels, washcloths, shampoo and soap before the bath.
- Make sure the room is warm.
- Use large towels that completely wrap around the person for privacy and warmth.
- Have a face cloth ready to cover the person's eyes to prevent stinging from water or shampoo.
- Make sure that soap and shampoo are easy to reach.
- Fill the bath and then assess the person's reaction to getting into the water.
- Monitor the water temperature; the person may not sense when the water is dangerously hot or may resist bathing if the water is too cool.

3. Focus on the person, not the task.

- Involve the person throughout each stage of the bath. Be sure the person has something to do, for example, have the person hold a washcloth or shampoo bottle.

- Give the person choices. For example, ask if he or she would like to bathe now or in 15 minutes, or take a bath or a shower.
- If the person resists bathing or acts out, distract him or her and try again later.
- Continuously praise the person for their efforts and co-operation.
- Protect the person's dignity, privacy and comfort.
- Cover or remove any mirrors if a reflection in the bathroom mirror leads the person to think there is a stranger present.
- Have a familiar person of the same sex to assist, if possible.
- Cover the shower seat and other cold or uncomfortable surfaces with warm towels.
- Have activities ready in case the person becomes agitated. For example, play soothing music or sing together.

4. Adapt the bathing process to meet the needs of the individual.

- Set a regular time of day for bathing. If the person usually has a bath or shower in the morning, it may confuse him or her to do this at night.
- Use simple phrases during the bathing process, such as, *'sit down', 'here is the soap', 'wash your arm'.*
- Use the 'watch me' technique, for example, put your hand over the person's hand, gently guiding the washing actions.
- Use a bath chair that can adjust to different heights so that the person can sit while showering if it is easier.
- Use a facecloth to wash and rinse hair in the sink to reduce the amount of water on the person's face.
- Ensure the person's genital area is washed, especially if incontinence is a problem.
- Ensure the person is washed between folds of skin and under the breasts.
- Never leave the person alone in the bathroom.
- Always check the water temperature, even if the person draws his or her own bath.
- Always put a non-slip mat in the bath or shower.
- Make full use of any grab rails.
- Make sure there are no puddles on the bathroom floor before you undertake any moving or handling.

5. Once the bath is completed:

- check for rashes or signs of pressure sores, especially if the person is incontinent or immobile and record these in the care plan
- seat the person while drying and putting on fresh clothes

- be gentle on the skin; the person's skin may be very sensitive; pat the skin dry instead of rubbing
- use cotton swabs to dry between the toes
- apply cream or lotion to keep the skin soft, or if incontinent apply a barrier cream to protect the skin.

A person with dementia will often forget how to comb their hair, clip fingernails or to shave. He or she may forget how nail clippers or a comb are used. Allow the person to use his or her favourite toothpaste, shaving cream, aftershave or makeup. Take a brush, comb your hair, and encourage the person to copy your movements. Remember to use cardboard nail files and electric shavers as these are less dangerous than nail clippers and wet-shave razors.

Ensuring that dentures and teeth are cleaned properly can help prevent infection, difficulty with eating as well as digestive disorders. However, oral hygiene is often problematic because a person with dementia may often be unaware of how or why it's important to take care of his or her mouth. The care worker should:

- provide short, simple instructions; breaking down each step by saying *'hold your toothbrush', 'put paste on the brush'*, then, *'brush your teeth'*
- use a 'watch me' technique: hold the toothbrush, show the person how to brush their teeth; or, put their hand over the person's hand, gently guiding the brush
- monitor daily mouth care: teeth or dentures should be brushed after each meal and teeth flossed daily; dentures should be removed and cleaned every night
- ensure the service user is visited by a dentist regularly and ask the dentist for suggestions that may help make dental care easier and more effective.

Choosing clothes and getting dressed can be very frustrating for people with dementia as they become overwhelmed with the choices or the task itself. Both the task of dressing and undressing and the process of choosing clothes needs to be simplified to avoid undue anxiety or panic. For example, try offering just two choices of shirts and trousers. Then lay out the clothing in the order that each item should be put on. Hand the person one item at a time while giving short, simple instructions such as *'put on your shirt'*, rather than *'get dressed'*. Choose comfortable and simple clothing. Cardigans, shirts and blouses that button in front are easier to work than pullover tops. Buttons or zips can often be too difficult to handle. These can be replaced with velcro fastners. Shoes should be comfortable. The soles should be non-slip and worn heels should be replaced to avoid falls. If the person wants to wear several layers of clothing, the care team should ensure he or she doesn't get overheated. Offer praise, not criticism, if clothing is mismatched. Be patient when assisting the person to dress as rushing the individual can cause anxiety and frustration.

Eating and drinking

Mealtimes can present many challenges for the care team. A person with dementia may have a poor appetite, loss of interest in food, may forget to eat or that they have already eaten. As a care worker you should ensure:

- that meals are served in a quiet place so that the person can focus on eating, for example, the television or radio should be turned off
- the table setting is kept simple, for example, remove flowers, centrepieces and condiments and only use the utensils needed for the meal
- that the person can distinguish food from their plate or bowl, for example, avoid highly patterned dishes, tablecloths and placemats
- that the food is at the correct temperature as the service user might not be able to tell if food or beverages are too hot to eat or drink
- flexibility in the choice and provision of food as service users often developed new food preferences or may reject foods they have previously enjoyed
- that the service user is given plenty of time to eat and remind him or her to chew and swallow carefully
- that the independence of the service users is encouraged by making the most of their abilities, for example, the person could eat from a bowl instead of a plate, or with a spoon instead of a fork and should use a 'watch me' technique. For example, hold a spoon and show the person how to eat a bowl of porridge.

Finally, the care worker should be aware that many individuals with dementia prefer finger foods, for example, fish fingers, potato wedges, cheese cubes, cherry tomatoes, etc. as these are easier to pick up with the hands and eat. Neatness is not important as the care worker should let the person feed himself, or herself as much as possible in the way they prefer.

Elimination

Alan's hospital experience:

'I was recently in hospital after suffering a mild heart attack. One day I wanted to go to the toilet. I asked to go but the nurse handed me a bottle. Unfortunately, I used it upside down and made the bed wet. The nurses were not pleased. I had to explain to them that I had a problem. They said they didn't know and I should have told them. But, surely, it must have been on my notes? It was very embarrassing for me. I had already told them I had Alzheimer's, but they didn't seem to know what it meant.'

(Alzheimer's Forum, 2009)

Many people with dementia have difficulty controlling bowel or bladder movements. They may be unable to recognise when they need to go to the toilet and they may forget where the bathroom is; or their difficulty might be the result of medication. If a person with dementia has recently started to lose control of his or her bladder and bowels, the first and most important step is to determine the possible causes, as follows:

1. Medical reasons

- Urinary tract infection, constipation or a prostate problem.
- Diabetes, stroke or a neuromuscular disorder such as Parkinson's disease.
- Physical disabilities that prevent the person from reaching the bathroom in time, for example, arthritis.

2. Effects of medication

- Sleeping pills and anxiety-reducing drugs may relax the bladder muscles.
- Drinks such as cola, coffee and tea can act as diuretics; a diuretic increases urination.
- Diuretic tablets, for example, frusimide, which are prescribed for heart failure will increase the frequency of urination.

3. Environmental or physical impediments

- Make sure the person can find the bathroom, for example, use appropriate signage.
- Improve access to the bathroom by removing any furniture or clutter that might be in the way and make sure the person's room is well lit.
- Provide clothes that are easy to remove, for example, use velcro fasteners instead of buttons or zips.

When dealing with problems with elimination, the care worker should be supportive by:

- Helping the person to maintain their dignity.
- Reassuring and encouraging the person to reduce any feelings of embarrassment they may have.
- Being matter of fact without scolding or making the person feel guilty, for example, by saying *'you've wet yourself again'*.
- Respect the person's need for privacy.

The care worker should provide the person with frequent prompts and reminders to use the toilet by:

- using adult words rather than child talk to refer to the process of using the toilet
- encouraging the person to tell you when he or she needs to use the toilet
- watching for clues such as restlessness, pacing, sudden silence, or hiding in corners or behind furniture; these clues could indicate the need to use the toilet
- learning the person's *'trigger'* words or phrases for needing to use the toilet ie. the person may use words that have nothing to do with the toilet , for example, *'I cannot find my way'* but to that person, it means going to the toilet.

Care workers should make it easy for the person to find and use the toilet by:

- posting a sign or a picture of a toilet on the bathroom door
- making the toilet door stand out by painting it a different colour to the walls
- ensuring that the toilet is safe and easy to use, for example, raising the toilet seat, installing grab bars on both sides of the toilet
- using a portable commode or urinal for night-time use, particularly if the person is less mobile
- removing waste bins or other objects that could be mistaken for a toilet.

The care team should monitor and record any incontinence, and then plan to reduce it by:

- reminding the person to use the bathroom just before his or her usual time
- identifying when incontinence occurs, then plan to avoid this, for example, if it happens every two hours get the person to the bathroom before that time
- setting a regular schedule for toileting, for example, first thing in the morning, every two hours during the day, immediately after meals and just before bedtime
- cutting down on drinks that stimulate urination such as cola, coffee, tea and grapefruit juice but don't withhold fluids as this could cause dehydration.

Lastly, care workers should:

- ensure that the person wears clothing that is easy to remove and to clean
- give the person plenty of time in the bathroom to empty his or her bladder and bowels
- run water in the sink or give the person a drink to stimulate urination
- check the toilet to see if the person has urinated or had a bowel movement
- help the person to clean their anal area, flush the toilet and wash their hands
- regularly wash any sensitive skin areas and apply a barrier cream if prescribed by the GP
- in consultation with the service user, family and GP, consider using incontinence aids.

The later stages of dementia

The late stage of dementia may last from several weeks to several months and intensive round-the-clock care is usually required. For the person, it is important to focus on preserving quality of life and dignity. He or she should always be treated with compassion and respect. A person with late-stage dementia can become bedridden. This inability to move around can cause skin breakdown, pressure sores and 'freezing' of joints (contractures). The care worker should relieve pressure and improve skin oxygenation by changing the person's position at least every two hours and keeping his or her limbs and joints in natural alignment. Pillows can be used to support arms and legs and to protect bony areas such as elbows, knees and hips. Emollients and creams should be gently applied rather than massaged into bony areas as vigorous rubbing can cause damage to the skin and increase the risk of pressure sore development. A range of passive movements in the joints should be maintained to prevent limb contractures. The care team should carefully and slowly move the person's arms and legs two to three times a day. A physiotherapist can advise regarding the proper method for passive exercises.

A person with late-stage dementia may experience incontinence for a number of reasons, including a urinary tract infection or faecal impaction. The care team should keep a written record of when the person urinates or defecates, and when and how much the person eats and drinks. This will help the care team identify the person's natural routine and a toileting schedule can then be planned around this. Incontinence products can be used at night to supplement the daytime toileting schedule. Bowel movements should be monitored and recorded in the care plan. It is not necessary for the person to have a bowel movement every day. However, if the person is constipated, natural laxatives such as prunes or whole-grain breads can be added to their diet or their fluid intake can be increased. If the person is taking codeine-based painkillers these may need to be reviewed by the GP as these can cause constipation.

A person with dementia may have trouble swallowing, which may cause food or drink to be aspirated into the airway and the lungs, which can lead to pneumonia.

The care team should allow plenty of time for eating and drinking. They should not rush the person or force him or her to eat or drink. They should make sure the person is in a comfortable, upright position and to help digestion, the person should remain in an upright position for 30 minutes after eating. Soft foods should be given as these can be chewed and swallowed easily. The person may prefer bite-sized finger foods, like slices of cheese, or chicken nuggets. If he or she can no longer eat solid foods, then these should be mashed or pureed in a blender. Liquids can be made easier to swallow by adding thickeners such as unflavoured gelatine to water, juice, milk, broth and soup. Difficulty in swallowing can lead to coughing and choking. The care team should be prepared for an emergency, and learn how to perform the Heimlich manoeuvre as well as how to use suction equipment to prevent aspiration. Weight loss should be monitored and although weight loss during the end-of-life stage is common, it may also be a sign of inadequate nutrition, another illness or medication side effects.

Increased immobility during the later stage of dementia can make a person more vulnerable to infections. The mouth and teeth should be kept clean as this reduces the risk of bacteria that can lead to infection. The care worker should brush the person's teeth after each meal. Alternatively, a moistened swab can be used to clean the gums, tongue and mucous membrane. Any abrasions or skin tears should be treated immediately and recorded in the person's care plan and the accident book. Wounds should be cleansed with warm soapy water and a sterile dressing applied. If the wound is deep, the GP should be contacted for assistance. Influenza can lead to pneumonia; it's vital for the person (and the care team) to get flu vaccines every year to help reduce this risk.

In the late stages of dementia, the person has more difficulty expressing pain. The care team should look for possible signs of pain such as pale skin tone; flushed skin tone; dry, pale gums; mouth sores. The care team should note the person's gestures, spoken sounds and the expressions on his or her face that may signal pain or discomfort. They should watch for changes in behaviour. Anxiety, agitation, shouting and sleeping problems can all be signs of pain. In addition, vomiting, feverish skin, or swelling of any part of the body can indicate illness, which should be reported to the GP.

Ideally, discussions about end-of-life care should take place while the person still has the capacity to make informed decisions. A person with dementia has the legal right to limit or forgo medical or life-sustaining treatment, including the use of mechanical ventilators, cardiopulmonary resuscitation, antibiotics and artificial nutrition and hydration. These wishes can be expressed through advance directives, provided the individual has capacity to make an informed decision. It is often very difficult for family members to accept refusal or withdrawal of treatment. However, aggressive medical treatment can often be detrimental to the quality of life of an individual when he or she is unfamiliar with their surroundings, or does not understand the intentions of the care providers.

ACTIVITIES, THERAPIES AND MEDICATION

Activities

As a carer you might be involved in assisting the person to:

- maintain independent movement, for example, through dance or gentle exercise
- reminisce, for example, using scrapbooks, photo albums or old magazines and encouraging conversation about these
- relax through music but you will need to keep noise level low – loud, distracting sounds could overwhelm the person
- undertake supervised indoor or outdoor activities like cooking, gardening or walking.

For the person with dementia, these activities will help to structure their time and distract them from repetitive behaviours. Activities will also enhance a person's sense of dignity and self-esteem by giving purpose and meaning to their life. However, it is important to make sure that your home supports the person's changing needs, and a balance has to be struck between maintaining the independence of service users and their safety during any of these activities. Therefore, when planning activities the care worker should:

- focus on the person
- consider the choice of activity
- consider the approach that might be used
- focus on creating a safe and supportive environment.

These issues are now presented in more detail:

Focus on the person

- Activities should be appropriate to the person and reflect his or her interests.
- The care workers need to keep the person's skills and abilities in mind.
- Attention needs to be paid to what the person enjoys.
- As a care worker, you will need to be aware of any potential physical problems, for example, restrictions in mobility.

Choice of activity

- The focus should be on enjoyment rather than achievement.
- The activity could relate to past work life and should relate to personal favourites.
- Consider the time of day, for example, is the person more mobile in the afternoon?
- Activities need to be flexible and adapted to the changing condition of the individual.
- Well-planned and collaborative activities can improve the quality of life of those with dementia.

The approach

- Offer support and supervision.
- Concentrate on the process, not the result.
- Be flexible and patient.
- Be realistic and relaxed.
- Help get the activity started.
- Break activities into simple, easy-to-follow steps.
- Assist with difficult parts of the task.
- Let the individual know he or she is needed.
- Stress a sense of purpose.
- Don't criticise or correct the person.
- Encourage self-expression.

Creating a safe and supportive environment

- Create a safe, comfortable and supportive environment for activities.
- If necessary, change the surroundings to encourage the activity.
- Minimise distractions that can frighten or confuse the person.

- Were there any times when there was too much going on or too little to do?
- Was the person bored or distracted?
- Identify the activities that worked best and those that didn't. Explain why, and record this in the care plan.

The use of alternative and complementary therapy

Herbs

Herbal medicine is the use of plants to restore or maintain health. Herbal medicines are generally regulated as foodstuffs or dietary supplements in the UK and they can be bought over the counter from most health food shops. It is important that a recognised brand, which is made by a leading manufacturer, is purchased as the quality and efficacy of these herbs may often vary. There are potential dangers with some forms of complementary and alternative medicines as some herbal preparations may interact harmfully with conventional drugs. It is, therefore, very important for the GP to know what herbs the person is taking as these might conflict with the person's prescribed medicines. According to the Alzheimer's Society (2009e) the following herbs have been shown to have a limited effect on the progression of Alzheimer's disease:

1. **Silymarin:** an extract of milk thistle, is a tall herb with prickly leaves and a milky sap. It may help the functioning of the liver and help reduce the side-effects experienced from conventional drugs that cause liver problems.
2. **Choto-san:** 'Kanpo' is a Japanese variant of Chinese traditional medicine. The 'Kanpo' mixture Choto-san, contains 11 medicinal plants and one research study found an improvement over 12 weeks in patients with vascular dementia taking Choto-san.
3. **Kami-umtan-to:** another Kanpo mixture, kami-umtan-to (KUT) contains 13 different plants and a recent clinical trial found a slower decline in dementia sufferers who were given this preparation.
4. **Yizhi capsule:** is a Chinese traditional herbal medicine; two studies used these capsules with patients who had vascular dementia and reported some degree of success.

Aromatherapy and massage

Aromatherapy is the therapeutic use of essential oils derived from plants. The oils are either applied directly to the skin, often accompanied by massage; or heated in an oil burner to produce a pleasant odour; or placed in a bath. According to the Alzheimer's Society (2009e) there is some evidence that aromatherapy with massage is effective in helping people with dementia to relax. It has also been found that excessive 'wandering' can be reduced by aromatherapy and massage. Also, it has been found that lavender oil can reduce agitated behaviour. The oils are provided in concentrated form and should be diluted according to the instructions when being used on the skin.

Conventional medicines

Most forms of dementia are incurable. However, some types of dementia can be controlled and drugs have been developed to give some temporary relief from symptoms. For example, people with Alzheimer's have been shown to have a shortage of the chemical acetylcholine in their brains. The drugs donepezil, rivastigmine and galantamine work by maintaining existing supplies of acetylcholine.

The National Institute of Health and Clinical Excellence (NICE) reviews drugs and decides whether they represent good enough value for money to be available as part of NHS treatment. The most recent NICE guidance on medication for Alzheimer's disease recommends that people in the moderate stages should be given treatment with donepezil (Aricept), galantamine (Reminyl) or anrivastigmine (Exelon).

The person must take these drugs as prescribed by the consultant. Usually the person will be started on a low dose, which will be increased later to maximise effectiveness. If the person misses a dose, they should take it as soon as they remember, if it is on the same day. If it is the next day, the person should not take two tablets but should simply continue with their normal dose.

If the person with dementia decides to stop taking a drug, they should speak to the doctor first if possible, or as soon as they can after stopping treatment. According to the Alzheimer's Society (2009f) if someone stops taking their prescribed drug, their condition will deteriorate over a period of about four to six weeks, until their symptoms are no better than in someone who has never taken the drug.

The most frequent side effects of Aricept, Exelon and Reminyl include:

- nausea and vomiting
- diarrhoea
- stomach cramps
- headaches
- dizziness
- fatigue
- insomnia
- loss of appetite.

According to the Alzheimer's Society (2009f) these side effects can be lessened if the person takes the lower prescribed dose for at least a month. Sometimes 'splitting' the dose, taking half in the morning and half later in the day can help, but the correct full daily dose must be maintained overall.

As discussed earlier in this chapter, people with dementia can sometimes develop mood disorders such as depression, restlessness, aggression, delusions and hallucinations. It is important to address the underlying causes that may have triggered a person's symptoms and drugs should be avoided unless they are really necessary. However, when these symptoms become severe, distressing, or when they are causing a risk to the person or others, it may be necessary to prescribe medication.

Medication to control depression, restlessness, aggression, delusions and hallucinations will be more effective if it is taken exactly as prescribed by the doctor, in the correct dose, and if it is monitored regularly for side effects. Therefore it is important for the person, the care worker and the family to appreciate that:

- any benefits from the medication can take several weeks to appear, particularly with antidepressants and antipsychotics
- some drugs, such as antidepressants and antipsychotics need to be taken regularly to have an effect
- all drugs have side effects that may worsen symptoms; these side effects are usually related to the dose
- the doctor will usually place the person on a low dose and then gradually increase this until the desired effect is achieved
- certain combinations of drugs may counteract each other, therefore, the GP must be informed if other medications are being taken
- a drug that has once proved to be useful may not continue to be effective; this is because dementia is a degenerative condition, so the chemistry and structure of the brain will change during the course of the person's illness
- once treatment has started, it is important that it is reviewed regularly, for example, drugs for behavioural problems should not be given for more than three months without a trial of stopping them.

Antipsychotics

Antipsychotics are the drugs most commonly used for the treatment of restlessness, aggression, delusions and hallucinations. According to the Alzheimer's Society (2009f) the two most common drugs that are used for Alzheimer's disease are risperidone and aripiprazole. They are not used for DLB or vascular dementia. The side effects are:

- excessive sedation
- dizziness
- unsteadiness
- shakiness, slowness and stiffness of the limbs
- chest infections
- ankle swelling
- falls.

According to the Alzheimer's Society (2009f) there is also the risk of more serious side effects such as a stroke or premature death. This risk becomes much higher over longer treatment periods and for those with DLB, or if the person is also being treated with sedatives. If taken for long periods, these drugs can produce side effects that include persistent involuntary chewing movements and facial grimacing.

Antidepressants

Symptoms of depression are common in dementia. According to the Alzheimer's Society (2009f) antidepressants such as fluoxetine may help in improving a persistently low mood. They may also be useful in controlling irritability and rapid mood swings. Once started, antidepressant drugs are usually given for a period of at least six months. However, in order for them to be effective, it is important that they are taken regularly without missing any doses. An improvement in mood usually takes two to three weeks or more to occur. Side effects may appear within a few days of starting treatment and may include:

- headaches
- nausea
- dry mouth
- blurred vision
- increased confusion
- constipation
- difficulty in urination
- dizziness on standing, which may lead to falls and injuries.

Anxiety states, panic attacks and fearfulness are also common amongst people with dementia. Mild symptoms are usually helped by reassurance, adjustments to the environment and the provision of a structure to the person's everyday life. More severe and persistent anxiety is often related to underlying depression, and usually improves with antidepressants. According to the Alzheimer's Society (2009f), Benzodiazepines for example, diazepam, are sometimes used but with extreme care due to the risk of dependency, which can lead to withdrawal symptoms when stopped. The side effects of these drugs are:

- excessive sedation
- unsteadiness and a tendency to fall
- increase confusion
- increased memory loss.

Hypnotics or sleeping pills

As already discussed, persistent wakefulness and night-time restlessness can be extremely distressing for the person with dementia. In addition, many of the drugs used for dementia can cause excessive sedation during the day, thus reducing a person's ability to sleep at night. Increased stimulation during the day and avoiding caffeinated drinks last thing at night will help reduce sleep problems. Aromatherapy with lavender can also help. It is important to have realistic expectations about what duration of sleep should be expected, for example, older people rarely sleep for more than five to six hours at night. Also, hypnotics are more helpful in getting people off to sleep, rather than keeping people asleep throughout the whole of the night. They are usually taken 30 minutes to one hour before going to bed and are best used intermittently, rather than regularly. If excessive sedation is given, the person may be unable to wake to go to the toilet and incontinence may occur. If the person does wake up during the night, increased confusion and unsteadiness may occur. According to the Alzheimer's Society (2009f) Zopiclone or Zolpidem are the sleeping tablets that are most commonly used as they have less of a hangover effect in the morning and are less addictive. The use of hypnotics should be regularly reviewed by the doctor.

SAFEGUARDING THE VULNERABLE PERSON

Older people who are dependent on others for their care needs are in a potentially vulnerable position, and may be at risk from those who might abuse the power and influence they have as a carer. It is the legal and moral responsibility of everyone working in a care home to respect the rights of service users and to protect them from physical or mental harm at all times. Failure to do so may constitute abuse.

Perpetrators of abuse can be any persons who are in a position of trust with a service user and may include partners, children or other relatives, carers, friends or neighbours, volunteer workers, professional health care staff or residential care staff themselves. Care workers should notice when service users are at risk from, or experiencing, neglect or abuse and respond appropriately to ensure that individual service users are protected. The factors that are known to contribute to abuse and exploitation include:

- prolonged stress amongst the care givers or care workers
- feelings of resentment and hostility towards the service user
- deeply held prejudices and stereotypes towards particular social groups, for example, the elderly
- financial dependency on the service user by a child or spouse
- unrestricted access to service user's finances by child or spouse
- poor levels of practical competence in caring for the older person
- inadequate monitoring or supervision of a carer or care worker.

Types of abuse and neglect

According to the *National Minimum Standards for Care Homes for Older People* (Department of Health, 2003a), the definition of abuse is that it is *'a single or a repeated act, omission or lack of appropriate action, occurring within a relationship of care or trust, which causes distress, harm or injury.'*

This definition allows several different types of abuse to be recognised including neglect, physical abuse, psychological abuse, sexual abuse, racial or cultural abuse and financial abuse. These are defined by the *National Minimum Standards for Care Homes for Older People* (Department of Health, 2003a), as follows:

Physical abuse: can take many forms including hitting, slapping, burning, pushing or restraining. Rough or careless handling may also constitute physical harm, as can giving too much medication or the wrong type of medication.

Neglect: occurs where a service user is not provided with adequate care or attention and suffers harm or distress as a result, for example, where a service user is deprived of food, water, heat, clothing, comfort or essential medication.

Psychological abuse: cruelty or verbal insults including shouting, swearing, frightening, blaming, ignoring, bullying or humiliating a person, even the spreading of rumours or malicious gossip. All service users should be able to live their lives with privacy, dignity, independence and choice and all information about them should remain confidential. The disclosure of confidential information, for example, by spreading stories or rumours about individuals could be regarded as psychological or emotional abuse.

Sexual abuse: occurs wherever a service user is forced to take part in any sexual activity without their prior consent. Sexual abuse can also take more subtle forms, and any sexual relationship between staff and service users can be considered to be abusive, even if the service user gives their consent. Sexual abuse may also occur when staff is giving personal care to a service user.

Financial abuse: the obtaining of money, valuable possessions, or property through cheating, or deception.

Racial or cultural abuse: often takes the form of discrimination, prejudice or insults.

However, in some care homes there may be an underlying culture that is indicative of abuse. Staff within these care homes often show a lack of concern or even contempt for service users and there may be a lack of flexibility or choice, a lack of privacy, a lack of respect, unjustified use of restraints, staff entering service user's rooms without due cause. There may also be restrictive practices full of petty rules and restrictions.

The signs of abuse and neglect

The following are possible signs that abuse might be occurring. However, it should be remembered that this is not a comprehensive list and other signs and symptoms might also be present. Also, the presence of one or more of these signs does not mean that there is absolute proof of abuse, rather it indicates that abuse might be occurring.

Physical abuse

- Unexplained bruises or cuts, especially where they reflect the shape of an object used, of a hand or of finger marks
- Loss of hair in clumps or abrasions on the scalp from hair pulling
- Unexplained fractures
- Unexplained burns or scalding
- Delays in reporting injuries
- Vague, implausible or inappropriate explanations
- Multiple injuries or a history of past injuries, especially falls

Neglect

- Debilitation or weakness through malnutrition or dehydration
- Unexplained weight loss

- Poor hygiene – unkempt, dirty appearance, clothes or surroundings
- Inappropriate dress
- Pressure sores
- Poor skin condition and poor resistance to infection and disease

Emotional abuse

- Fearfulness
- Mood changes including depression, irritability and unhappiness
- Low self-esteem
- Changes in sleep and appetite patterns
- Withdrawn, self-isolating behaviour

Financial abuse

- Unexplained loss of money or inability to pay bills
- Sudden withdrawal of large amounts of money
- Sudden disappearance of favourite or valuable possessions
- Loss of pension or building society books etc.

Sexual abuse

- Unexplained difficulty in walking
- Bleeding or bruised genitals
- Reluctance to be alone with a particular person
- Sudden changes in behaviour

Responding to abuse and neglect

The immediate safety or health of the victim is the first concern. Staff should talk to the victim and assess the situation, summoning help, giving first aid and calling for medical support, an ambulance or the police as necessary. If the abuser is still present, staff should attempt to calm the situation, but should not place themselves at risk.

If the situation is not an emergency, all suspicions and events should be reported to the person in charge. The person in charge should then investigate the suspicion by collecting evidence and by talking to the service user. Tact and sensitivity are important in this process and it may sometimes be necessary for a member of staff known to the service user to talk to them rather than the person in charge.

In situations where the service user says that they will tell the member of staff but asks the member of staff not to tell anyone else, the care worker should advise the service user that they cannot keep that confidentiality and must by policy inform the manager or person in charge. However, they should reassure the victim that their information will be treated as confidential and that the home will not necessarily proceed with an investigation without their consent – unless there has been a criminal act and the law has been broken, or unless the alleged abuse involves others at risk.

Consent is vital. In general, the victims of abuse do not have to take action against their abuser and have the right not to. This is particularly common where the abuser may be a son or a daughter or another member of the family. If the suspected victim does not want the incident to be taken further, their wishes must be respected unless the victim is:

- in physical danger
- incapable of making an informed decision themselves
- not the only person at risk.

The underlying rule is that a person has the right to decide how they want to be helped – or if they want to be helped at all. Where a service user is considered incapable of making an informed decision or of giving consent, the person in charge should discuss the situation with close relatives or guardians. Possible risks and outcomes need to be explained carefully to the victim so that an informed decision can be made.

All cases of abuse where the victim gives consent should be referred to social services without delay. In situations where there is evidence of a criminal act the case should be reported immediately to the police by the manager or person in charge. This is particularly important in suspected sexual abuse where the police will want to gather forensic evidence, for example, DNA, as rapidly as possible. Referral to the police or social services should include the following information:

- personal details of the victim
- the referrer's details
- the substance of the allegation
- details of the alleged abuser
- details of incidents or events including dates, places, injures, witnesses
- whether or not consent has been given to take the matter further.

Once a referral has been made, social services will then work to its own guidelines and procedures and care home staff should ensure that they co-operate. All facts, incidents, assessments and discussions related to the suspicions should be recorded clearly and accurately in the service user's care plan as soon after the incident as possible. Opinion should be avoided and only facts should be reported. Such records are strictly confidential and should be kept securely and safely according to the Data Protection Act (1998). They may be used as evidence in a future criminal investigation.

Where no referral to social services is made, in line with the victim's wishes, then alternative courses of action should be considered and the service user given appropriate support. In the case of a member of staff being the alleged abuser, the home should proceed with disciplinary action and an internal investigation in line with the home's disciplinary policy. The action of the staff member may constitute grounds for dismissal through gross misconduct even if no criminal case is pursued. Here it should be remembered that the burden of proof in civil law is not as stringent as that in criminal law. Careful notes should be kept outlining the exact suspicions and the action taken. In the case of a relative or carer being the alleged abuser, the home may arrange with the service user to restrict visits or to have only accompanied visits. In all cases, the situation should be carefully monitored.

Local social services departments will always be willing to advise individual care homes who have suspicions of abuse and there are several organisations who run confidential help lines and offer similar advice. Homes must also be prepared to accept that in some cases of abuse, little action can be taken beyond continued support, recording and monitoring due to limitations in the law and the victim not wanting to proceed. However, in all cases detailed written records should be kept in a secure place and all staff should work together to minimise the risk of further abuse.

Once a referral has been made to social services a care assessor or social worker will investigate and an assessment will be made of the needs of the victim and the victim's carers. A case conference may well then be arranged and a package of care and support set in place as appropriate. Social services will work hand in hand with the police throughout this process and may continue to monitor the situation for some time.

The police, for their part, have a duty to investigate any possible criminal offences that will include interviewing victims, witnesses and suspects and gathering evidence. This process may not always end in criminal proceedings, but early involvement will give the police the best opportunity to conduct their investigations effectively. Cases of suspected sexual abuse should always be reported to the police immediately.

National minimum standards for the prevention of abuse and neglect

The *National Minimum Standards for Care Homes for Older People* (Department of Health, 2003a) states that:

- arrangements for health and personal care ensure that service users' privacy and dignity are respected at all times
- all staff use the term of address preferred by the service user
- all staff are instructed during their induction on how to treat service users with respect. Where service users have chosen to share a room, screening is provided to ensure that their privacy is not compromised
- service users should be enabled to exercise their legal rights
- service users must be safeguarded from physical, financial, material, psychological, sexual or discriminatory abuse, or abuse through neglect,

self-harm or degrading treatment, through deliberate intent, negligence or ignorance.

The *National Minimum Standards for Care Homes for Older People* (Department of Health, 2003a) also states that:

- Procedures should be in place for responding to suspicion or evidence of abuse or neglect (including whistle-blowing) in accordance with the Public Interest Disclosure Act (1998) and Department of Health (2000) guidance: *No Secrets.*
- All allegations and incidents of abuse should be followed up promptly and the action taken recorded.
- Staff who may be unsuitable to work with vulnerable adults are referred, in accordance with the Care Standards Act (2000), for consideration for inclusion on the Protection of Vulnerable Adults' register.
- Physical or verbal aggression by service users is understood and dealt with appropriately by staff and physical intervention or restraint is used only as a last resort.
- Service users have access to their personal financial records, can safely store their money and valuables, are free to consult on their finances in private and free to gain advice on personal insurance.
- Staff should not be involved in assisting the making of or benefiting from service users' wills.

Where service users control their own money then the *National Minimum Standards for Care Homes for Older People* (Department of Health, 2003a) states that the following must be in place:

- safeguards to protect the interests of the service user
- written records of all transactions are maintained
- where the money of individual service users is handled, the manager ensures that the personal allowances of these service users are not pooled and appropriate records and receipts are kept
- the registered manager may be appointed as agent for a service user only where no other individual is available
- secure facilities are provided for the safe keeping of money and valuables on behalf of the service user
- records and receipts are kept of possessions handed over for safe keeping.

Remember!

- Older people who are dependent on others for their care needs are vulnerable to abuse and exploitation.
- Abuse often arises as a result of an imbalance of power between the service user and care giver.
- Older people may suffer from a number of different types of abuse, neglect and exploitation. These might include physical, sexual, financial or emotional.
- Be aware of the possible signs and symptoms of abuse.
- Always follow the policies and procedures of your care home when responding to any concerns about abuse, neglect or exploitation.
- Any concerns regarding suspected or alleged abuse or neglect must be reported to a supervisor or senior manager immediately.
- The issue of service user consent is key to any investigation of alleged abuse or exploitation. Therefore, care workers must ensure that allegations of abuse or exploitation are handled sensitively and in a confidential manner.

End of chapter quiz

1. List three changes in communications that a person with dementia might experience.

2. List three ways in which communications with this person might be improved.

3. List three possible causes of aggression.

4. List three possible causes of night-time restlessness.

5. List three possible causes for 'wandering'.

6. List the drugs that are recommended by NICE for the treatment of moderate stage Alzheimer's disease.

7. Give three side effects of antipsychotic drugs.

8. When carrying out massage, what should you do before you apply any essential oil to the skin?

9. List the five main types of abuse.

10. List three factors that are known to contribute to the abuse and exploitation of older adults.

✍ My continuing professional development (CPD) log

Name of care worker ....

Name of manager/supervisor ....

Name of employer ....

Start date for dementia care training...

Expected date of completion ....

This is to confirm that .... [*name of care worker*] has satisfactorily completed..................... [*insert number*] of hours of study, and has achieved all of the following learning activities:

1. discuss the need for positive and effective communications with the individual with dementia, for example, listening, responding, encouraging
2. describe the importance of maintaining the health, safety and well-being of the individual with dementia, for example, mobility, nutrition, personal care etc.
3. outline activities, therapies and medication that may be used to help individuals with dementia, for example, prescribed and alternative or complementary therapies
4. outline the principles of safeguarding vulnerable people.

Comments from care worker or supervisor, for example, outcomes of key learning activities or results of quiz.

Signed (care worker): .... Date:...............................

Signed (supervisor): .... Date:...............................

Chapter four

Roles, boundaries and legal frameworks

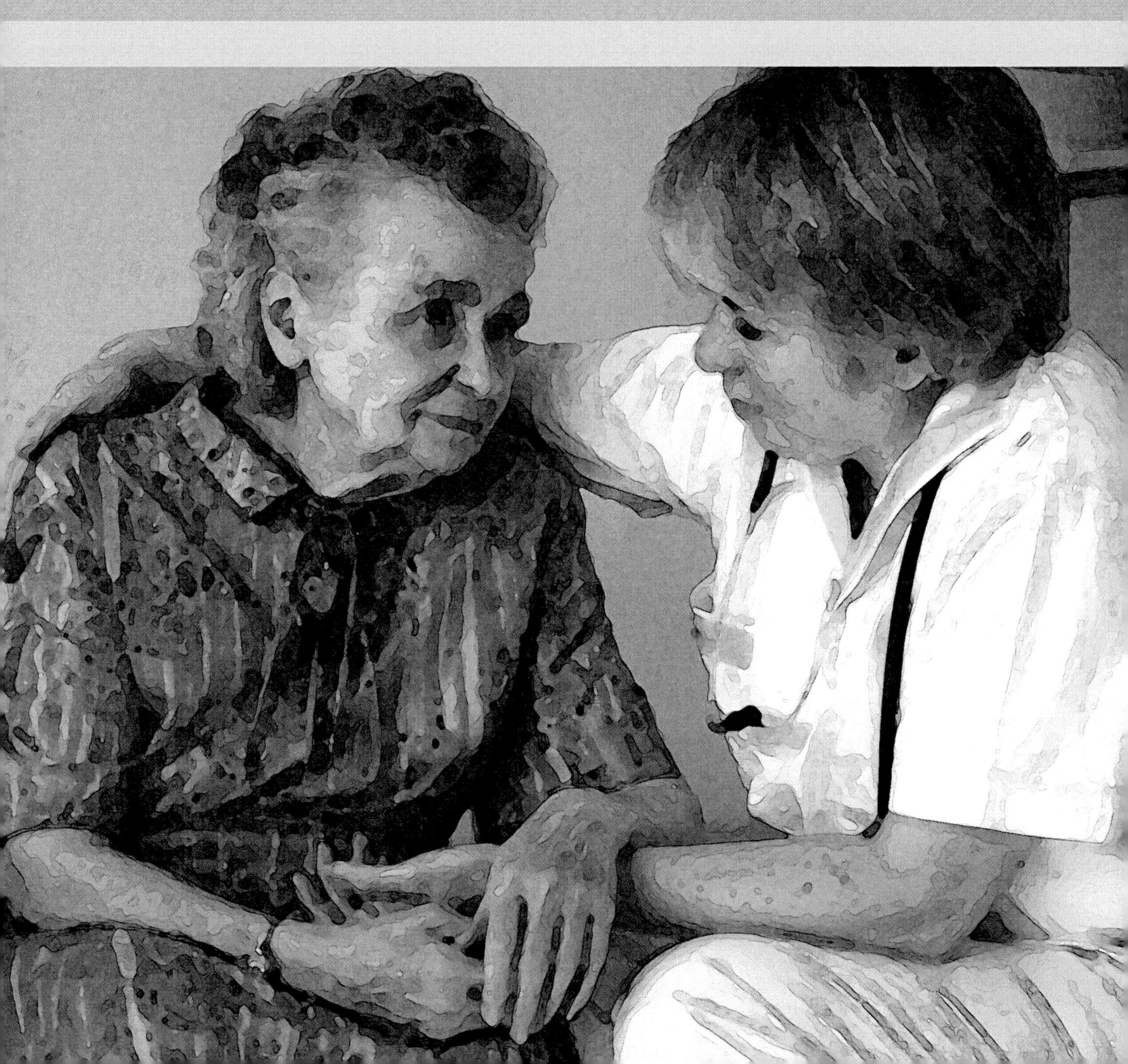

Chapter four

Roles, boundaries and legal frameworks

☺ Key learning activity

This activity will provide you with key background information before you read the final chapter. Make a note of your answers and discuss these with a colleague or your supervisor before you commence with your reading.

Q1. Indicate which professional would best meet the needs of an individual in the following situations:

- an individual at home is having difficulty in getting in and out of their bath
- an elderly service user is having difficulty in swallowing and is losing weight
- a new service user is unsteady on his feet
- an individual is restless and starting to wander at night
- a residential service user has a discharging ulcer on his leg that requires daily dressings.

Q2. Where would you record the following information?

- A service users has refused their medication.
- Transport has been confirmed for a service user to attend the x-ray department.
- A relative has left some money for her mother's hairdressing appointment.
- There has been an overnight change in the condition of an elderly service user.
- The way in which a service user should be transferred from chair to toilet.
- A frail service user has fallen over and sustained an injury.
- A service user's risk of pressure ulcer development.
- A service user's weight.

Q3. Produce an information sheet for individuals new to the service explaining their rights relating to the following:

- individual rights relating to information kept about them
- what the law states on obtaining and keeping information on individuals
- how the organisation's confidentiality policy protects the privacy and security of information obtained from individuals
- how information is shared within the care team.

AIMS OF THE CHAPTER

At the end of this chapter, the learner will be able to:

- identify the roles, responsibilities and boundaries of carers and how teamwork and support can lead to better support of individuals with dementia
- discuss the importance of communicating, reporting and recording effectively the care of individuals with dementia, for example, differences between subjective and objective observation; clear concise and accurate reporting; avoiding stereotypes and use of negative language
- identify the roles and responsibilities of services and organisations in relation to dementia care, for example care homes, hospitals, respite care, domiciliary care, informal carers, support groups
- explain the legislation and guidance relevant to individuals with dementia for example, Human Rights Act (1998); Mental Capacity Act (2005); *National Service Framework for Older People* (Department of Health, 2001) etc.
- Discuss the organisation's visitors policy, and *No Secrets* policy, and how to apply these with regard to people with dementia.

ROLES, RESPONSIBILITIES AND BOUNDARIES OF CARE PROVIDERS

A wide range of health and social care services are available to people with dementia, and to those who care for them. The services available and the way they are organised, vary from area to area. Most are arranged through the NHS or through social services. Some are provided by voluntary organisations and may also be available privately.

The care of a person with dementia is highly complex and involves meeting the physical, mental and social needs of an individual. Therefore, in order to gain a broad understanding of an individual's requirements, the person, their family and the following professionals work very closely together to undertake a needs assessment. Once these needs are known, they are shared with the multidisciplinary team to ensure that services are prioritised to meet the holistic needs of the individual.

General practitioner or GP

The first person that the individual or family are likely to consult is the GP, who will often arrange a home visit. It is easier to assess and observe a person's behaviour in their own home, as it then becomes clearer exactly what the problems are. The GP will assess the person by undertaking:

- an analysis of the individual's family and job history, and social background to try and establish just what the symptoms are
- physical examinations and tests, for example, an examination of the nervous system and heart and blood and urine tests, to identify other conditions that may be causing confusion
- tests of mental function and reasoning, for example, the GP may ask a series of questions designed to test thinking and memory.

At the end of the assessment, the GP may feel able to make a diagnosis, or they may wish for a specialist assessment to be undertaken.

Consultant

A consultant will have more specialised knowledge and experience of dementia than the GP, and will have access to more specialised investigations, such as brain scans. The type of referral may depend on the age of the person, their symptoms and what is available in the individual's locality.

The main types of consultants are as follows:

- **neurologist** – he or she will specialise in disorders of the brain and nervous system; some neurologists have particular experience in diagnosing dementia
- **geriatrician** – he or she will specialise in the physical illnesses and disabilities associated with old age and in the care of older people
- **psychiatrist** – he or she will specialise in diagnosing and treating a wide range of mental health problems
- **psycho-geriatrician** – he or she is a psychiatrist who has specialised in the mental health problems of older people, including dementia.

The consultant works with a specialist team of other doctors who have undergone various stages of training in their particular speciality. The consultant also works with other health care professionals such as nurses, psychologists, occupational therapists and social workers. Each of these brings their own unique knowledge, skills and advice to the dementia care team.

Community mental health nurses

Community mental health nurses are mental health nurses who have had further training to work in the community. They provide nursing care and support for people with mental health problems and dementia. They carry out assessments of people at home and can advise on ways of coping, and of improving their health and quality of life. Community mental health nurses can be contacted via the GP's surgery.

District nurses and community nurses

District and community nurses are members of the primary care team. District and community nurses have had extra training in order to nurse people at home. You can contact a district nurse via the family GP.

Health visitors

Health visitors are nurses who have had further training to advise people in the community on preventing illness. They can provide information on local services and suggest ways of keeping well. They can also keep the person in touch with services such as carers' groups, when they identify a need. Health visitors usually work with the family GPs.

Practice nurses

Practice nurses work with GPs and other community nurses and carry out a range of nursing activities within the GP practice.

Social workers

Social workers have specific professional training and qualifications and are registered with the General Social Care Council. They are involved in assessing the need for services, and in planning, co-ordinating and advising on services for people with dementia. Some social workers are also referred to as 'care managers' and may be based in social services departments, hospitals and care homes. Social workers can be contacted via the local social services department.

Social care workers

Social care workers work in a wide variety of settings and are known by a variety of names. For example, some work as 'home care workers' in the person's home, or in care homes as 'residential care workers'. They may help with personal care, such as getting the person out of bed, washing and dressing them, changing the person's bedding and emptying their commode, doing their laundry and supervising their meals to make sure the person eats properly, and putting them to bed at night. Social care workers require extensive on-the-job training and all new workers must complete the Skills for Care Common Induction Standards followed by a Level 2 NVQ in Care. Those who have completed the Level 4 NVQ Registered Managers Award (or its equivalent) will manage the delivery of social care services, either through a domiciliary care agency, or in a residential care setting.

Physiotherapists

Physiotherapists are responsible for assessing an individual's functional ability, such as walking and general mobility. They often work closely with occupational therapists and are also able to give advice on the risk of falls and safe methods of moving and handling.The GP or consultant can refer the person to the community physiotherapy service or the hospital physiotherapy department.

Occupational therapists

The occupational therapist is responsible for assessing the person's ability to carry out their activities of daily living. Once an assessment is completed, they can then advise on aids, adaptations and equipment to help the person become more independent. A referral can be made by the family GP.

Chiropodists

Problems with painful feet or deformed or inflamed toes can increase the risk of immobility for someone with dementia. NHS chiropody services can be arranged through the GP.

Audiologists

Problems with hearing can increase the risk of confusion for someone with dementia. Audiologists check for hearing problems and can fit a hearing aid, if appropriate. Hearing tests and hearing equipment are free on the NHS. The GP will refer the person to the nearest NHS hearing centre while the dementia is at an early stage.

Dentists

Problems with dentition can increase the risk of malnourishment for someone with dementia and professional dental advice should be obtained as soon as dementia is diagnosed. Dentists can also provide advice to carers about oral hygiene during the later stages of dementia. The family dentist may be able to arrange home visits. If not, the community dental service (CDS) will look after people who need treatment at home. NHS home visits are free, but the normal charges for treatment may apply, depending on income.

Optometrists

Problems with sight can increase the risk of confusion for someone with dementia. The person's eyesight should be checked regularly by an optometrist, who will also examine the eyes for signs of glaucoma, cataract and other eye and medical conditions. You will need to find an optometrist who understands what examining someone with dementia may involve. Some will carry out a home visit. People aged over 60, and some under-60s who have dementia, are entitled to a free NHS eye examination.

Speech and language therapists

Problems with swallowing can increase the risk of malnutrition for someone with dementia. Speech and language therapists work closely with the dietician as they assess an individual's swallowing capabilities and advise on ways of relieving any swallowing difficulties. They may also provide advice and guidance on how to communicate more effectively with people who have dementia. The family GP can make a referral, or the local speech and language department can be contacted directly.

Dieticians

People with dementia are at risk of malnutrition. A dietician can provide advice and guidance about food, nutrition and issues such as a poor appetite, weight loss, weight gain, vitamins and food supplements. The GP will make a referral to the dietician.

Clinical psychologists

Clinical psychologists assess memory, learning abilities and other skills, and offer support. They often work with consultants in memory clinics, as part of the multidisciplinary team.

ROLES AND RESPONSIBILITIES OF ORGANISATIONS THAT PROVIDE SERVICES

Local authority social services departments are the main providers of care and support services for people with dementia. If a person with dementia is in need of support, they should contact the local social services department to explain their situation. The department will then carry out a needs assessment and identify what services are appropriate to meet those needs. This is known as a *'community care assessment'*.

If the department assesses a person as being in need of services, it has a legal duty to provide the services that fall within their sphere of responsibility. However, the person may have to contribute towards the cost of these services. Local authorities can provide the services themselves, or they may make arrangements for private or voluntary sector organisations to provide care on their behalf. The views and preferences of the person receiving the service are always taken into account.

If, after assessing the person's needs, the social services department agrees that certain services should be provided, it will provide the person with a written care plan outlining these services. This applies whether the person lives at home or in residential care. The care plan is reviewed regularly as the needs of a person with dementia are likely to change rapidly. A review can be initiated if the person, the family GP, or the care team contacts the local social services department.

Once the social services department has confirmed the services that the person is likely to receive, the person and their family can begin to think through the possible options. A key decision will be whether the person wishes too, and can remain in their own home, or whether they would prefer to move into sheltered housing or a care home.

It is also important for the person (and their family) to consider the financial implications of the options available and social services will be able to give an idea of how much the person will have to pay towards the costs of the various services that have been agreed. However, services provided by the NHS, such as community nursing, are still free.

Staying at home

If the person with dementia is staying in their own home, there are a number of points for them and their family to consider. These include:

Financial assistance

A check should be made that all available benefits are being claimed. Extra benefits for the person with dementia can make a great deal of difference to them and their family.

Special equipment

Does the person require equipment such as an elevated toilet seat, a walking frame, or a commode to make it easier for them to stay in their home?

Special adaptations

Does the person need a wheelchair ramp, a walk-in shower, or grab rails close to the toilet to enable them to remain in their home?

Assistance with activities of living

Does the person require meals on wheels, help with shopping, cooking or other domestic tasks? Social services can arrange these services or put you in touch with a domiciliary care agency. The GP can arrange nursing care.

Respite and family support

Does the person or their family require a befriending scheme, home care, or day care, or respite care to help relieve the stress associated with giving personal care at home? Social services will be able to arrange either of these services.

Sheltered accommodation

This enables people to continue to live independently but with the reassurance that help is at hand. It can be suitable for some, but not all, people with dementia as any move to new surroundings is likely to increase a person's confusion, and no sheltered scheme can offer the constant monitoring and support that is available in residential care.

There are many different types of sheltered accommodation. Some include a community warden who lives on the premises who can be contacted by means of an alarm. Others, such as 'extra care' or 'very sheltered' housing schemes will provide domestic help and the provision of meals. There are also some schemes that offer accommodation on the same site as a care home, and these also provide some care services within the same residential complex.

The person can continue to receive services that they have been assessed as needing in sheltered accommodation in the same way that they can at home.

Residential care

Almost all care homes that offer residential care are run privately or by voluntary organisations, although some are run by local authorities. Also, almost all care homes that offer nursing care are run privately or by voluntary organisations, although the NHS run a few. Some homes are able to provide both residential and nursing care. Residential homes provide personal care for helping with dressing, washing, going to the toilet and taking medicine. Nursing homes always have a trained nurse on duty and provide 24-hour nursing care in addition to personal care. Nursing care is provided if the person is confused and frail, has difficulties with mobility, has other chronic debilitating illnesses, or is incontinent of urine or faeces. Sometimes a person with dementia who needs intensive care may be eligible for free continuing NHS health care. The GP or consultant will advise on this.

COMMUNICATING, REPORTING AND RECORDING EFFECTIVELY

Dementia is a condition that changes rapidly. Therefore, it is important for the care team to keep a person's condition under constant review and to communicate this to the person, members of his or her family and the multidisciplinary team. Recording changes in an individual's condition is an important part of the care team's work and may include activities such as:

- informing colleagues of any changes in a person's condition
- evaluating any care that has been given
- recording compliance with medication
- recording the wishes of the person with dementia
- undertaking risk assessment to ensure the health and safety of the individual.

This will involve the completion of several different types of documentation, for example, daily handover reports, care plans, medication record sheets, risk assessment documents etc.

The quality of what is recorded in these documents is very important. In particular, entries should be fact-based and written objectively, and in order to write objectively care workers must learn to separate their personal beliefs and opinions from fact.

In addition, the words and expressions that a care worker uses to convey everyday meanings are important. Words can convey negative images of individuals, for example, people who have a disability are often called 'handicapped'. This can lead to an assumption that disabled people are damaged versions of 'normal' people. As a care worker, you should avoid making stereotypical judgements about the potential ability of individuals with dementia.

Principles of good record keeping

Care plans, needs assessments, case reviews and day files are required as legal records of care and the keeping of certain confidential notes and records relating to individual service users are an essential part of the communication and day-to-day running of a care home. According to the NHS Confidentiality Code of Practice, care records should:

1. **be factual, consistent and accurate** ie. they should be:

- written as soon as possible after an event has occurred, providing current information on the care and condition of the service user
- written clearly, legibly and in such a manner that they cannot be erased
- written in such a manner that any alterations or additions are dated, timed and signed in such a way that the original entry can still be read clearly
- dated accurately, timed and signed or otherwise identified, with the name of the author being printed alongside the first entry
- readable on any photocopies ie. care records should be written in black ink
- written, wherever applicable, with the involvement of the service user
- clear, unambiguous, (preferably concise) and written in terms that the service user can understand

- written so as to be compliant with the Race Relations Act and the Disability Discrimination Act.

2. **be relevant and useful** ie. they should:

- identify problems that have arisen and the action taken to rectify them
- provide evidence of the care planned, the decisions made, the care delivered and the information shared
- provide evidence of actions agreed with the service user (including consent to care and/or consent to disclose information).

3. **care records should *not* include:**

- unnecessary abbreviations or jargon
- meaningless phrases, irrelevant speculation or offensive subjective statements
- irrelevant personal opinions regarding the service user.

Legislation and record keeping

The rules governing the recording and use of service user information has been laid down by the Caldicott Report (Department of Health,1995). The key requirements of this report are that the care worker must:

1. justify a purpose for recording and using service user information
2. only record and use information when it is absolutely necessary
3. use only the minimum information required
4. only access information on a strict 'need to know' basis
5. be aware of his or her responsibilities concerning the recording and use of service user information
6. understand and comply with the law, for example, the Data Protection Act.

The *National Minimum Standards for Care Homes for Older People* (Department of Health, 2003a) states that care workers should be fostering an atmosphere of openness and respect, in which residents, family, friends and staff all feel valued and that their opinions and rights matter. This can be done in the case of record keeping by encouraging staff to involve the service user whenever records are being written. If this is done then not only can the service user be more actively involved in their own care, but the need for the recording can be explained and understood. By developing an atmosphere of 'working together' with the service user, anxieties will be greatly reduced.

Standard 37 of the *National Minimum Standards for Care Homes for Older People* (Department of Health, 2003a) relates to the degree to which service users' rights and best interests are safeguarded by a home's record keeping policies and procedures. Specific standards include the following.

1. Records required by regulation for the protection of service users and for the effective and efficient running of the business are maintained, up-to-date and accurate.
2. Service users have access to their records and information about them held by the home, as well as opportunities to help maintain their personal records.
3. Individual records and home records are secure, up-to-date and in good order; and are constructed, maintained and used in accordance with the Data Protection Act (1998) (DPA) and other statutory requirements.

The Data Protection Act (1998)

The Data Protection Act (1998) (DPA) sets standards governing the storage and processing of personal data held in manual records and on computers. The act works in two ways – giving individuals (data subjects) certain rights, whilst requiring those who record and use personal information (data controllers) to be open about their use of that information and to follow sound and proper practices (the data protection principles). All residential or nursing care homes that hold manual or computerised service user or employee records are covered by the Data Protection Act (1998). According to the Data Protection Act (1998), there are eight main principles under which personal data should be kept and collected. Personal data should:

- be obtained fairly and lawfully
- be held for specified and lawful purposes
- be processed in accordance with the person's rights under the DPA
- be adequate, relevant and not excessive in relation to that purpose
- be kept accurate and up-to-date
- not be kept for longer than is necessary for its given purpose
- be subject to appropriate safeguards against unauthorised use, loss or damage.

One of the most important aspects of the DPA is that personal data may be processed only if the service user has given his or her consent. All files kept about residents or staff should be confidential and, according to the Data Protection Act (1998) service users should know what records are being kept about them and why they are being kept.

Also, service users should be given access to what is said about them in any personal records maintained by the home and information should be withheld only in exceptional circumstances. All data, and particularly sensitive or confidential data, must be stored securely. Manual records such as personnel files and resident care files should be kept in locked filing cabinets, preferably within an office that is locked when unattended. Care must be taken when working on confidential files that they are put away securely and not left out on a desk when people could walk by and see them. Where data is stored electronically on a computer, the following steps should be considered:

1. check regularly on the accuracy of data being entered (remember that a home may be liable for inaccurate or erroneous data)
2. ensure that the computer system is secure by checking that it has a backup system, that lost data can be recovered and that backups are stored in a safe and secure place
3. ensure that all staff who need to use the computer system are thoroughly trained in its use
4. ensure that passwords are being used for access to different parts of the system, that these are regularly changed and not abused by being passed on to people who should not have them
5. use screen blanking to ensure that personal data is not left on screen when not in use by authorised staff
6. review the terminal positions to ensure that unauthorised staff or service users cannot casually view personal data on screen
7. ensure that confidential or private print-outs are stored securely and safely and that they are collected immediately if printed onto a networked printer.

With regard to the use of service user records, the NHS Confidentiality Code of Practice for record keeping states that the care worker should ensure that records are:

- formally booked out from their normal filing system
- tracked if transferred, with a note made or sent to the filing location of the transfer
- returned to the filing location as soon as possible after use
- stored securely within the clinic or office, arranged so that the record can be found easily if needed urgently
- kept closed so that when not in use the contents are not seen accidentally
- inaccessible to members of the public and not left even for short periods where they might be looked at by unauthorised persons
- held in secure storage with clear labelling. Protective 'wrappers' indicating sensitivity – though not indicating the reason for sensitivity – and permitted access, and the availability of secure means of destruction, for example shredding, is essential.

With regard to electronic records, the *NHS Confidentiality Code of Practice* (Department of Health, 2003b) states that care staff must:

- always logout of any computer system or application when work on it is finished

- not leave a terminal unattended and logged-in
- not share logins with other people
- not reveal passwords to others
- change passwords at regular intervals to prevent anyone else using them
- avoid using short passwords, or using names or words that are known to be associated with them (for example children's or pet's names or birthdays).
- always clear the screen of a previous patient's information before seeing another use a password-protected screensaver to prevent casual viewing of patient information by others.

Finally, please remember!

1. Accurate and timely record keeping is essential to good care practice.
2. Care records, for example, observation charts, records of daily activities, risk assessment charts and care plans etc. are all legal documents. You must complete them in a clear, accurate and objective way.
3. You must be familiar with and always follow your employer's policies and procedures on what, where, when and how to complete individual care records.
4. Observing the rules concerning the appropriate storage, security and disclosure of care records will ensure that the service user information will remain confidential.

LEGISLATION AND GUIDANCE RELEVANT TO INDIVIDUALS WITH DEMENTIA

It is very important that you have an understanding of how legislation might affect the care of people with dementia because:

- there will be many aspects of your work that are governed by current law
- many laws form the basis of your workplace policy and procedures
- you are responsible for ensuring that the rights of people with dementia are protected
- you need to know what action to take if the rights of service users are abused.

Legislation and codes of practice that relate to vulnerable people are underpinned by the following values and principles ie. people with dementia have the right to be:

- protected from harm
- treated with dignity and respect

- treated equally
- free from discrimination.

In addition, people who have dementia (and their family) need protection from the law so that they:

- can manage their finances and property
- determine which care services are most suited to the person's needs
- can make autonomous decisions about personal matters, while they still have capacity
- make advance decisions about future care provision
- can take action when care falls below an acceptable standard
- can take action if the person is being treated differently on the grounds of their dementia
- can take action if the person is refused access to funding or services
- can take action if the person is in an unsafe environment.

The Enduring Power of Attorney Act (1985)

The Enduring Power of Attorney Act (1985) (EPA) gives the person with dementia a legal right to choose one or more people to act on their behalf to manage their financial affairs. However, the person must do this while he or she still has the mental capacity to make decisions, for example, during the early stages of dementia. Once the application has been made, the person can continue to manage their own finances until they are no longer able to do so, at which time a further notification is required. The Mental Capacity Act (2005) extended these powers by creating a new type of power of attorney, known as a lasting powers of attorney (LPA). LPAs replaced EPAs in 2007, when the Mental Capacity Act came into force. There are two types of LPA:

- **a property and financial affairs** *LPA* gives an attorney the power to make decisions about financial and property matters, for example, selling a house or managing a post office account
- **a personal welfare LPA** gives an attorney the power to make decisions about health and personal welfare, such as day-to-day care, or where the person should live.

Further information can be obtained from: www.opsi.gov.uk.

The Human Rights Act (1998)

The rights of individual service users are protected by the Human Rights Act (1998). If an individual feels that their rights have been breached by a public authority, or voluntary or private organisation they can bring a case against them. Therefore, carers must work according to the principles of the act. These include:

- the right to life
- freedom from torture and degrading treatment
- freedom from slavery and forced labour
- the right to liberty
- the right to a fair trial
- the right not to be punished for something that wasn't a crime when you did it
- the right to respect private and family life
- freedom of thought, conscience and religion, and freedom to express your beliefs
- freedom of expression
- freedom of assembly and association
- the right to marry and to start a family
- the right not to be discriminated against in respect of these rights and freedoms
- the right to peaceful enjoyment of your property
- the right to an education
- the right to participate in free elections
- the right not to be subjected to the death penalty.

Further information can be obtained from: www.opsi.gov.uk.

The Community Care Act (1990)

The aim of this act was to enable people to live independently within the community. It placed a legal duty on the local authority to carry out an assessment of needs, and to produce a plan of care once these needs were identified. Services could include home care, day care, respite care, residential care, as well as adaptations or special equipment for the home. Further information can be obtained from: www.opsi.gov.uk.

The Disability Discrimination Act (1995)

The Disability Discrimination Act (1995) (DDA) was extended in 2005 and it now gives disabled people rights in the areas of employment, education, access to goods, facilities and services. The act requires public bodies to promote equality of opportunity for disabled people. It also gives disabled people important rights of access to health services and social services, such as doctor surgeries, dental surgeries, hospitals and mobile screening units. The provisions of the act mean that a person's GP should not refuse to register, or to continue treating that person, because of their disability. The act also means that the person has a right to information about health care and social services in a format that is accessible to them. For example, a hospital may provide forms and explanatory literature in large print or braille to assist people with visual impairments, or arrange for a sign language interpreter for someone with a hearing impairment. Further information can be obtained from: www.opsi.gov.uk.

The Health Act (1999)

This act rationalised health and social services budgets by pooling them together. This encouraged more joint working between health and social care agencies, which meant that both care services could be delivered to people with dementia in a much more meaningful way.

Further information can be obtained from: www.opsi.gov.uk.

THE CARE STANDARDS ACT (2000)

The Care Standards Act (2000) (CSA) placed responsibility for regulation of residential care, nursing homes, adult placement and domiciliary support under a single national agency, the Commission for Social Care Inspection (CSCI). The act specifies national minimum standards for residential care homes, adult placement and domiciliary care agencies. For example, the *National Minimum Standards for Care Homes for Older People* (Department of Health, 2003a) list important outcomes for the provision of care that must be achieved by owners of residential and nursing homes. These include:

- choice of home
- health and personal care
- daily life and social activities
- complaints and protection
- environment
- staffing
- management and administration.

The CSA also made provision for any reports arising from an inspection of residential homes to be made publicly available through the CSCI's website. The Commission for Social Care Inspection merged with the Healthcare Commission in April 2009 and the new body is known as the Care Quality Council. Further information can be obtained from: www.opsi.gov.uk or www.cqc.org.uk.

The National Service Framework for Older People

The National Service Framework for Older People (Department of Health, 2001) sets out good practice guidelines for the care of older people. The framework sets out eight main areas for improvement.

- Dealing with age discrimination
- Person-centred care
- Intermediate care
- General hospital care
- Stroke

- Falls
- Mental health
- The promotion of health and healthy living

The Mental Capacity Act (2005)

The Mental Capacity Act (2005) provides a statutory framework to empower and protect adults who lack the mental capacity to make decisions for themselves because of illness, a learning disability, or mental health problems. According to the law, a person is defined as being unable to make decisions if they are not able to:

- understand information given to them
- retain that information long enough to be able to make a decision
- weigh up the information available to make a decision
- communicate their decision through whatever means appropriate.

The act is based on five main principles:

1. Every adult has the right to make their own decisions and must be assumed to have capacity to do so unless it is proved otherwise.
2. All reasonable help and support should be provided to the person so that they make their own decisions before it can be assumed that they have lost capacity.
3. It should not be assumed that someone lacks capacity simply because their decisions might seem unwise or eccentric.
4. If someone lacks capacity, anything done on their behalf must be done in their best interests.
5. Before making a decision on the person's behalf, all reasonable alternatives must be considered and the final option that is chosen should have the least impact on their human rights.

Further information can be obtained from: www.opsi.gov.uk.

Advance decisions

The Mental Capacity Act (2005) gives people the right to make an advance decision, which allows the person with dementia to state what types of treatment they do and do not want, should they lack the mental capacity to decide this for themselves at some time in the future. This may include refusal of life-sustaining treatment. Advance decisions are legally binding and must be followed by all members of the multidisciplinary team.

An advance decision cannot be made to request a particular treatment, it can only specify what types of treatments would be refused. An advance decision is legally binding if it is made in writing, signed by the person making it and is witnessed. The person making the decision must be aged 18 years or over and must have the mental capacity to make such a decision. The person must clearly state which treatments they are refusing and to which circumstances the refusal refers.

The writing of an advance decision statement can bring some reassurance to a person worried about their future health care. Also, when the multidisciplinary health care team are faced with difficult decisions about what treatment to give, an advance decision will help to ensure that the person's wishes are taken into account. The act of preparing the statement will also open up a dialogue with doctors and nurses that might otherwise be delayed until it is too late. It can also assist family and close friends by relieving them of some of the burden of decision-making.

The Mental Health Act (2007)

The Mental Health Act (2007) covers people who have been diagnosed with a 'mental disorder'. If a person is thought to be a risk to themselves or to others, or if their health is at risk, they can be detained in hospital. This is known as 'being sectioned'. The act:

- gives the authority for someone to be detained in hospital for assessment, for a maximum of 28 days
- gives the authority for someone to be detained in hospital for treatment; to start with, a person can be kept in hospital for six months; after this time, the section may be renewed for a further six months, and then for a year at a time
- also deals with aftercare arrangements; it means that the statutory authorities have a duty to make arrangements for the person's continuing support and care.

Only an approved social worker or a person's nearest relative can apply for a person to be sectioned under the Mental Health Act. Two medical officers must have seen the patient within the past 14 days and within five days of each other, and they must confirm the need for a section in their medical reports.

If a person has a mental disorder and lacks mental capacity, a court can appoint a 'guardian' for them. This arrangement is known as a 'guardianship order'. The guardian has powers and responsibilities to make decisions on behalf of the person lacking capacity. However, guardianship can only be arranged if an approved social worker or the person's nearest relative applies for it, and if two doctors agree to it. Usually, the local authority is named as the guardian, although a friend or relative may be appointed. The guardian has the power to require:

- the person to live at a specified place
- to require the person to attend a specified place for medical treatment
- that access be given to the patient by a doctor or approved social worker.

The guardian cannot detain the person or restrict his or her movements. The guardian cannot authorise medical treatment, and has no control over the person's financial affairs. The guardian must always act within the best interests of the person, failure to do so could result in criminal proceedings. Further information can be obtained from: www.opsi.gov.uk.

ORGANISATIONAL POLICIES AND PROCEDURES

The role of policies and procedures

A policy is an official document that gives information about what must be done in your place of work. It sets out the standards that you must achieve, and gives a clear indication of your responsibilities in relation to them. For example, there will be a manual handling policy that outlines the health and safety laws and regulations with which you have legally to comply. This will include information about standards for safe working practice with regard to manual handling: for example, the need to undertake a risk assessment before moving a heavy load.

A procedure is a document that explains how you should do your job, for example, it translates policies into working practice. Procedures are based on workplace values and principles to ensure that the job is done properly. For example, a manual handling procedure will tell you exactly how to undertake a risk assessment, covering all the stages in the process. It is very important that you follow the policies and procedures in your care home. In doing so, you will be:

1. encouraging good practice
2. maintaining the health and safety of staff, service users and their families
3. obeying the law.

Remember, you are legally responsible for the safety of service users and co-workers, and for ensuring that the policies and procedures in your workplace are followed correctly. You are required to do so by a number of laws and regulations that govern practice in the workplace. They include:

- Health and Safety at Work Act
- Health and Safety (First Aid) Regulations
- Food Safety Act
- Fire Precautions Regulations
- Manual Handling Operations Regulations
- Control of Substances Hazardous to Health Regulations
- Reporting of Injuries and Dangerous Occurrences Regulations.

☺ Activity: How might each of these laws influence policy and procedure at work?

1. Health and Safety at Work Act
2. Manual Handling Operations Regulations
3. Control of Substances Hazardous to Health Regulations (COSHH)
4. Reporting of Injuries, Diseases and Dangerous Occurrences Regulations (RIDDOR)

Record your answers below and then discuss these with your supervisor.

1. Health and Safety at Work Act

2. Manual Handling Operations Regulations

3. Control of Substances Hazardous to Health Regulations (COSHH)

4. Reporting of Injuries and Dangerous Occurrences Regulations (RIDDOR)

Policies applicable to people with dementia

As indicated in the learning objectives at the beginning of this chapter, the following policies will be discussed:

1. Visitors
2. *No Secrets* (Department of Health, 2000)

Each of these will now be covered in more detail.

1. Visitor policy

Standard 13 of the *National Minimum Standards for the Care of Older People* (Department of Health, 2003a) states service users should able to have visitors at any reasonable time and in accordance with their preferences. This means that:

- people with dementia should be able to receive visitors in private
- people with dementia should be able to choose whom they see and do not see
- the care team should not impose restrictions on visits except when requested to do so by the person, whose wishes are recorded
- relatives, friends and representatives of service users should be given written information about the home's policy on visiting.

CASE STUDY ONE: THE PINES NURSING HOME

The Pines operates a policy of open visiting, although the most convenient visiting times are generally between 11am and 8pm, when there will also be a member of staff available for the visitor to speak to if necessary. At other times of the day, staff tend to be busy and their priority must be the residents.

The manager and deputy manager will also be available between 10am and 5pm, and visitors are encouraged to call in at the office for a chat at any time. If in doubt, by all means contact us first for an appointment.

For a change of scene perhaps, the Anchor pub is only one minute walk from the Pines, along a flat path with good wheelchair access, and offers good pub food and a lovely garden.

Visitors' observations and suggestions are always welcome.

Visitors are asked to sign in and out when visiting.

A quiet room is also available upon request when visiting.

At the Pines, all staff are approachable and keen to resolve any problems.

CASE STUDY TWO: THE GRANGE NURSING HOME

SCOPE: resident/client family members/friends, volunteers, and all other individuals who conduct business on the Grange premises.

AIMS: To ensure visitors are knowledgeable of health and safety policies relative to their presence at the Grange and to protect residents, staff, visitors and the property of the facility, the Grange has developed the following policy:

1. All visitors to the Grange shall report to the reception desk during work hours or to the nursing units at other times.
2. All visitors should acquaint themselves with the Grange's mission and values, the floor plan and emergency exits. (This information is available at the main entrance, reception desk and nursing stations.)
3. Visitors to the Grange shall conduct themselves in a safe and appropriate manner.
4. All visitors must respect the privacy of others by keeping their personal and/or medical information (verbal, written, or any other form) private and confidential.
5. All interactions with residents, staff, other visitors and pets must be conducted with respect.
6. All visitors will agree to assisting and maintaining a healthy and safe environment:

- the Grange could be experiencing isolated cases of infections such as gastrointestinal or respiratory infections, all visitors will practice infection prevention and control measures as advised by management and/or nursing staff
- all visitors will wash their hands (use alcohol rub provided) upon entering and leaving the facility
- all visitors must use and wear personal protective equipment as required by health and safety standards
- visitors who are ill (ie. cold, flu) should call nursing units prior to visiting
- in the event of an outbreak, visits to the facility will be restricted
- visitors will identify themselves to staff and clarify with staff appropriate aspects of care pertaining to the resident they are visiting (ie. food, drink, medication, hands-on involvement).

7. Visitors must obey the following rules of conduct at all times:

- follow all verbal instructions and signs
- do not touch or attempt to operate any care centre's equipment, machine, or device unless authorised to do so
- stay out of restricted areas.

8. Visiting hours are from 8.00am–9.00pm, seven days a week. Exceptions are at the discretion of the registered nurse.
9. Children accompanying visitors must be supervised by an adult at all times.
10. Pets accompanying visitors must be leashed and in control.
11. The Grange is a non-smoking environment for visitors. Visitors cannot smoke in the facility or anywhere on the grounds.
12. Any injury, hazard, or problem, no matter how minor, must be reported to staff immediately.
13. Visitors are encouraged to share their concerns with staff.
14. In the event of emergency, all visitors must report to the reception desk or nursing station.
15. Visitors who fail to follow these policies will have their visiting privileges revoked and be asked to leave. The Grange shall not be responsible for injuries visitors suffer as a result of violating these rules.

Note: In our effort to maintain a home-like environment for our residents, the Grange houses pets such as a cat, birds and fish.

☺ Activity: Visitor policies

Read the two case studies on the Pines and the Grange nursing homes, and using the table below, compare each home's policy on visitors.

In your opinion:

- How would you rate each home regarding the health, safety and security risks to service users ie. poor, fair, good, or excellent?
- How would you rate each home regarding the confidentiality, dignity and privacy of service users ie. poor, fair, good, or excellent?

Based on your rating, which care home would you place an elderly relative who has dementia?

	The Pines	**The Grange**
Health		
Safety		
Security		
Confidentiality & Privacy		
Dignity		

Which care home would you place your relative in, and why?

2. No Secrets

No Secrets was published by the Department of Health in 2000. The aim of this report was to create a framework for action, which all responsible agencies (including residential care homes) should adopt to ensure a coherent policy for the protection of vulnerable adults at risk of abuse. The Care Standards Commission (now the Care Quality Commission) has since published guidelines for the protection of frail and vulnerable people who are living in care homes. These are listed in the *National Minimum Standards for Care for Care Homes for Older People* (2003) and are reflected in Standard 18, which states that *'18.1. The registered person ensures that service users are safeguarded from physical, financial or material, psychological or sexual abuse, neglect, discriminatory abuse or self-harm, inhuman or degrading treatment, through deliberate intent, negligence or ignorance, in accordance with written policies.'*

The *National Minimum Standards* (2003) (NMS) also state that the home must:

- have robust procedures for responding to suspicion or evidence of abuse or neglect to ensure the safety and protection of service users, including whistle-blowing
- ensure that all allegations and incidents of abuse are followed up promptly and any action taken is recorded
- ensure that staff who may be unsuitable to work with vulnerable adults are referred, in accordance with the Care Standards Act, for consideration for inclusion on the Protection of Vulnerable Adults register
- ensure that the home's policies and practices regarding service users' money and financial affairs allow service users to manage their personal financial affairs and exclude staff from benefiting from service users' wills.

As a consequence of the NMS guidelines, many care homes have now developed internal safeguarding policies and procedures that:

- include a statement of commitment to a zero tolerance of abuse and neglect within their organisation
- provide guidance on minimising and preventing abuse
- state what to do in an emergency
- are consistent with the local multi-agency safeguarding adults' policy, procedure and guidance
- provide details of who is responsible for referring in your organisation
- detail key responsibilities for the referrer
- provide telephone number and details of how to make a referral
- provide a copy of the local inter-agency alert form
- detail key responsibilities for alerters, ie. their duty to ensure a person's safety and well-being and to report.

- reference the role of staff and volunteers
- provide appropriate and accessible information for services users
- provide a cross reference to other internal policies and procedures within the organisation, for example, domestic violence, serious incidents, health and safety, disciplinary policies etc.

☺ Activity: How does your *No Secrets* policy measure up?

Use the following checklist to assist you in appraising your organisation's own policy and procedures. Discuss your answers with your supervisor.

1.	Our policy and procedures include a statement of commitment to a zero tolerance of abuse and neglect within our organisation.
2.	Our policy and procedures include guidance on minimising and preventing abuse.
3.	Our policy and procedures are consistent with the local multi-agency safeguarding adults policy, procedures and guidance.
4.	Our policy and procedures provide details of what to do in an emergency.
5.	Our policy and procedures provide the correct names of people in our organisation who are responsible for making a referral.
6.	Our policy and procedures detail the key responsibilities for the referrer in line with the multi-agency procedure.
7.	Our policy and procedures provide telephone numbers and details of how to make a referral.
8.	Our policy and procedures include copies of the referral pro forma, or its computer file location that is accessible to referrers.

9.	Our policy and procedures detail key responsibilities for alerters in line with the multi-agency procedure.
10.	Our policy and procedures provide information about the role of staff and volunteers in relation to safeguarding adults.
11.	Our policy and procedures offer relevant information for service users, families and carers and/or information about where this can be obtained.
12.	Our policy and procedures have been cross-referenced with our other internal policy and procedures and are compatible.
13.	Our policy and procedures have details of who is responsible for ensuring that they are updated when necessary.

Source: (City of York and North Yorkshire Adult Protection Committee, 2009).

End of chapter quiz

1. What is an advanced decision?

2. What is a guardianship?

3. List three principles of the Data Protection Act that govern the recording of personal data:

4. What is a policy?

5. What is a procedure?

✍ My continuing professional development (CPD) log

Name of care worker ....

Name of manager/supervisor ....

Name of employer ....

Start date for dementia care training..

Expected date of completion ....

This is to confirm that .... [*name of care worker*] has satisfactorily completed...................... [*insert number*] of hours of study, and has achieved all of the following learning activities:

1. discuss the need for positive and effective communications with the individual with dementia, for example, listening, responding, encouraging
2. describe the importance of maintaining the health, safety and well-being of the individual with dementia, for example, mobility, nutrition, personal care etc
3. outline activities, therapies and medication that may be used to help individuals with dementia, for example, prescribed and alternative or complimentary therapies
4. outline the principles of safeguarding vulnerable people.

Comments from care worker or supervisor, for example, outcomes of key learning activities or results of quiz.

Signed (care worker): .... Date:..............................

Signed (supervisor): .... Date:..............................

References

Alzheimer's Forum (2004) *When I first realised that something was wrong* [online]. Available at: www.alzheimersforum.org (accessed Sept 2009).

Alzheimer's Forum (2005) *Other people's perceptions* [online]. Available at: www.alzheimersforum.org (accessed Sept 2009).

Alzheimer's Forum (2007a) Barry: *Tell us the truth* [online]. Available at: www.alzheimersforum.org (accessed Sept 2009).

Alzheimer's Forum (2007b) *Barry's 10 tips for staying positive* [online]. Available at: www.alzheimersforum.org (accessed Sept 2009).

Alzheimer's Forum (2007c) Janet: *My doctor's appointment* [online]. Available at: www.alzheimersforum.org (accessed Sept 2009).

Alzheimer's Forum (2007d) Keith: *Simple as ABC* [online]. Available at: www.alzheimersforum.org (accessed Sept 2009).

Alzheimer's Forum (2008a) *What changes I notice in myself as a result of the illness* [online]. Available at: www.alzheimersforum.org (accessed Sept 2009).

Alzheimer's Forum (2008b) *How do you cope with sleepless nights?* [online]. Available at: www.alzheimersforum.org (accessed Sept 2009).

Alzheimer's Forum (2008c) Bill: *Laughing at dementia and why not?* [online]. Available at: www.alzheimersforum.org (accessed Sept 2009).

Alzheimer's Forum (2009) *Alan's hospital experience* [online]. Available at: www.alzheimersforum.org (accessed Sept 2009).

Alzheimer's Society (2009a) *What is dementia? Factsheet 400* [online]. Available at: www.alzheimers.org.uk (accessed Sept 2009).

Alzheimer's Society (2009b) *What is Alzheimer's disease? Factsheet 401* [online]. Available at: www.alzheimers.org.uk (accessed Sept 2009).

Alzheimer's Society (2009c) *What is dementia with Lewy bodies* (DLB)? Factsheet 403 [online]. Available at: www.alzheimers.org.uk (accessed Sept 2009).

Alzheimer's Society (2009d) *What is fronto-temporal dementia (including Pick's disease)?* Factsheet 404 [online]. Available at: www.alzheimers.org.uk (accessed Sept 2009).

Alzheimer's Society (2009e) *Factsheet 434* [online]. Available at: www.alzheimers.org.uk (accessed Sept 2009).

Alzheimer's Society (2009f) *Drug treatments for Alzheimer's disease Factsheet 407* [online]. Available at: www.alzheimers.org.uk (accessed Sept 2009).

City of York and North Yorkshire Adult Protection Committee (2009) *Safeguarding Adults in North Yorkshire Multi-Agency Policy and Procedures.* Version 1.0: May.

Dementia Care Central (2009) *Care Givers Story* [online]. Available at: www.dementiacarecentral.com (accessed Sept 2009).

Department of Health (1995) *The Caldicott Committee: Report on the review of patient-identifiable information*. London: The Stationery Office.

Department of Health (2000) *No Secrets: Guidance on developing and implementing multi-agency policies and procedures to protect vulnerable adults from abuse*. London: Department of Health.

Department of Health (2001) *National Service Framework for Older People*. London: Department of Health.

Department of Health (2003a) *National Minimum Standards for Care Homes for Older People*. London: The Stationery Office.

Department of Health (2003b) *Confidentiality: NHS Code of Practice*. London: The Stationery Office.

Help the Aged (2008) *Supporting a Good End of Life. My home life*. Issue 6, October.

Kitwood T (1993) *Towards a theory of dementia care: The interpersonal process. Ageing and Society*. Cambridge: Cambridge University Press.

Skills for Care (2009) Qualifications and Training: Qualification and Credit Framework QCF [online]. Available at: www.skillsforcare.org.uk (accessed Sept 2009).

Appendix

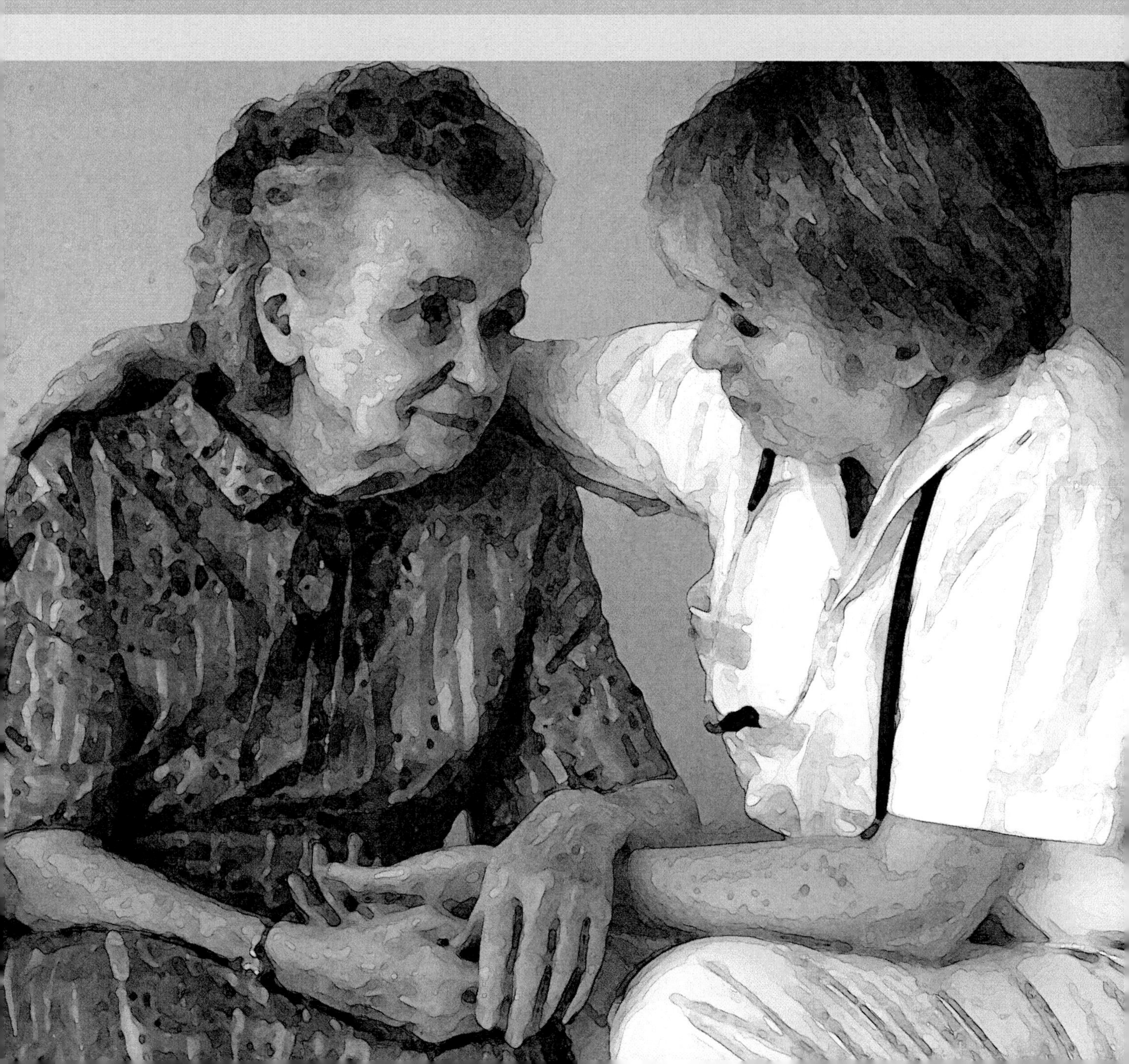

Appendix

ANSWERS

Chapter one quiz answers

1. **According to the Alzheimer's Association (2009a) how many people in the UK suffer from dementia?**
   700,000

2. **What are the most common types of dementia?**
   Alzheimer's disease, Lewy bodies disease, vascular disease, frontro-temporal dementia

3. **What is vascular dementia?**
   If the vascular system within the brain becomes damaged and blood cannot reach the brain cells, the cells will die. This can lead to the development of vascular dementia.

4. **What is DLB?**
   Dementia with Lewy bodies (DLB)

5. **Nightmares and hallucinations are symptoms most commonly associated with which type of dementia?**
   DLB

6. **Which type of dementia is most commonly associated with memory loss?**
   Alzheimer's disease

7. **Which type of dementia is most commonly associated with changes in personality and language difficulties?**
   Frontro-temporal, for example, Pick's disease

8. **Why is a brain scan of an individual undertaken?**
   To rule out a stroke; a brain tumour; or a collection of fluid on the brain.

9. **What is a psycho-geriatrician?**
   A psychiatrist who has specialised in the mental health problems of older people, including dementia.

10. **What is meant by mild cognitive impairment (MCI)?**
    Some individuals may have difficulty remembering to do things, but their symptoms may not be as severe as some forms of dementia.

Activities

Other people's perceptions:

The stereotypes we have of older and infirmed people, for example, helpless and incapable.

My dad:

Plans ahead; distracts; talks soothingly

Barry's 10 tips for staying positive:
Acceptance, he is beginning to adapt and make changes to compensate for his loss, for example his tips for others.

Chapter two quiz answers

1. **Complete the following sentence: 'Fundamental to the person-centred approach is the need to recognise a person's: culture, ------------'.**
   Feelings, individuality, need for privacy, need for respect
2. **What are the four stages of grief?**
   Denial, anger, rationalisation, acceptance.
3. **What are the three steps for dealing with an emotional outburst?**
   Reassure, respond, refocus
4. **List three community care services that are available to service users with dementia.**
   Home care services, equipment and adaptations, day care services, short breaks (respite) in a care home or a person's own home, residential care
5. **Who are the Alzheimer's Society and what do they do?**
   A care and research charity for people with dementia and those who care for them. Their helpline provides information, support, guidance and referrals to other appropriate organisations.

Chapter three quiz answers

1. **List three changes in communications that a person with dementia might experience.**

   Difficulty finding the right words
   Inventing new words to describe familiar objects
   Easily lose their train of thought; difficulty organising and sequencing words
   Frequent use of swear words
   Speaking less often or becoming mute
   More often relying on gestures instead of speaking
2. **List three ways in which communications with this person might be improved.**

   Always approach the person from the front and introduce yourself
   Call the person by their name as it will orientate the person and get their attention
   Let the person know you are listening and are trying to understand what is being said
   Maintain eye contact as this shows the person that you care about what is being said
   Focus on the feelings behind the words rather than content of the sentence
   Avoid criticising, correcting or arguing with the individual
   Ask the person to point or gesture if you don't understand what is being said
   Talk slowly and clearly, using simple words and sentences
   Use simple rather than complicated questions and ask questions one at a time

Allow the person extra time to think about your question before they give an answer
Understand that there may be a need to repeat information and questions
Give responses in a clear and concise way

3. **List three possible causes of aggression.**

Lack of rest or sleep
Side effects from their medication
Experiencing pain or other physical symptoms such as a full bladder
Upset caused by loud noises, a busy environment, or large crowds
Feeling lost or disorientated
Asking too may questions or giving too many explanations at once
Explanations and instructions may not be simple and easy to understand
The person picking up on your own anxiety, stress, or irritability
Being judgemental or critical of the person

4. **List three possible causes of night-time restlessness.**

Less need for sleep, which is common among older adults
An upset in the 'internal body clock' causing a mix-up between day and night
Disorientation due to an inability to separate dreams from reality when sleeping

5. **List three possible causes for 'wandering'.**

Side effects of medication
Confusion related to time
Restlessness and agitation
Stress or anxiety
Inability to recognise familiar people, places and objects
Fear arising from the misinterpretation of sights and sounds
A need to fulfil former roles and responsibilities, such as going to work or looking after a child

6. **List the drugs that are recommended by NICE for the treatment of moderate stage Alzheimer's disease:**
donepezil (Aricept), galantamine (Reminyl) and anrivastigmine (Exelon)

7. **Give three side effects of antipsychotic drugs.**

Excessive sedation
Dizziness
Unsteadiness
Shakiness, slowness and stiffness of the limbs
Chest infections
Ankle swelling
Falls

8. **When carrying out massage, what should you do before you apply any essential oil to the skin?**
   Dilute the oil according to instructions.

9. **List the five main types of abuse.**
   Emotional, financial, neglect, physical, sexual

10. **List three factors that are known to contribute to the abuse and exploitation of older adults.**

    Prolonged stress amongst the care givers or care workers
    Feelings of resentment and hostility towards the service user
    Deeply held prejudices and stereotypes towards the elderly
    Financial dependency on the service user by a child or spouse
    Unrestricted access to service user's finances by child or spouse
    Poor levels of practical competence in caring for the older person
    Inadequate monitoring or supervision of a carer or care worker

Activities

HOW MIGHT EACH OF THESE LAWS INFLUENCE POLICY AND PROCEDURE AT WORK?

1. **The Health and Safety at Work Act (1974)** lays down the duties of employers and employees. Under this act, the employer has to protect the health, safety and security of staff, service users and visitors. In order to do this, the employer is required to draw up safety policy and procedures, and to make arrangements for these policies and procedures to be carried out, and then regularly reviewed. Also, employers have to provide:

1. a safe working environment
2. safe access to and from the workplace
3. information on health and safety
4. health and safety training
5. a risk assessment of potential hazards.

The employee has a responsibility to:

1. take reasonable care of his or her own health and safety as well as the health and safety of others, such as the service users and their visitors
2. co-operate with his or her employer on health and safety issues
3. ensure that any health and safety equipment is not intentionally damaged.

2. **The Manual Handling Regulations (1992)** were introduced to reduce the number of injuries from moving and handling activities. The term 'manual handling' includes the lifting, moving, putting down, pushing, pulling and carrying by hand or bodily force of goods, equipment and people. An employer must avoid moving and handling where there is a risk of injury to staff, assess the risk of injury from moving and handling and reduce the risk of moving and handling. An employee must make full and proper use of the manual handling systems and equipment provided.

3. **The Control of Substances Hazardous to Health Regulations (1999) (COSHH)** have been put in place to protect against harmful substances. In particular, COSHH states that employers must:

- ensure safe storage and disposal of substances that are harmful to health
- check that health hazards from all substances are assessed, including the laundry, kitchen and outdoors
- ensure appropriate control measures are implemented
- ensure staff are trained about safe procedures and use of protective clothing
- check that procedures for spillages are in place
- check that new staff is trained before using substances.

Before any substances are used in the workplace, employers must undertake the following risk assessment:

- What substances are present and in what form?
- What harmful effects are possible?
- Where and how are the substances stored, used and handled?
- Are harmful fumes produced, especially if products are mixed?
- Can a safer substance be used?
- Who could be affected, to what extent, for how long and under what circumstances?
- How likely is it that exposure will happen?
- Are precautions required, such as ventilation and protective equipment?

Your care home will have a COSHH protection file. This will tell you what protective clothing you should wear (if any), how to store any hazardous substances, and how to dispose of any hazardous substances, for example, used needles should be placed in a yellow sharps box.

4. **The Reporting of Injuries, Diseases and Dangerous Occurrences Regulations (1995)** came into force on 1 April 1996. RIDDOR requires the reporting of work-related accidents, diseases and dangerous occurrences. It applies to all work activities, but not to all incidents. Reporting accidents and ill health at work is a legal requirement. The information that is reported enables the enforcing authorities to identify where and how risks arise and to investigate serious accidents. The enforcing authorities can then help and advise on preventive action to reduce injury, ill health and accidental loss. Your employer needs to report any deaths; major injuries; accident or injury resulting in over three days' loss of work, and any diseases, dangerous occurrences and gas incidents. All accidents, diseases and dangerous occurrences can be reported to the incident contact centre (www.riddor.gov.uk/info.html) your employer must keep a record of any accident, reportable injury, disease or dangerous occurrence. The record must include:

1. the date and method of reporting
2. the date, time and place of the event
3. personal details of those involved
4. a brief description of the nature of the event or disease.

Any accidents that occur at work must be recorded in an accident report book. The details contained in this document are confidential and must comply with the Data Protection Act (1998).

Chapter four quiz answers

1. **What is an advanced decision?**

The Mental Capacity Act (2005) gives people the right to make an advance decision, which allows the person with dementia to state what types of treatment they do and do not want, should they lack the mental capacity to decide this for themselves at some time in the future. This may include refusal of life-sustaining treatment. Advance decisions are legally binding and must be followed by all members of the multidisciplinary team.

2. **What is a guardianship?**

The Mental Health Act (2007) states that the court can appoint a 'guardian' for a person with a mental disorder, who lacks mental capacity. The guardian has powers and the responsibility to make decisions on behalf of the person lacking capacity. The guardian has the power to require:

- the person to live at a specified place
- to require the person to attend a specified place for medical treatment
- that access be given to the patient by a doctor or approved social worker.

The guardian cannot detain the person or restrict his or her movements. The guardian cannot authorise medical treatment, and has no control over the person's financial affairs. The guardian must always act within the best interests of the person.

3. **List three principles of the Data Protection Act that govern the recording of personal data:**

Information must:

- be obtained fairly and lawfully
- be held for specified and lawful purposes
- be processed in accordance with the person's rights under the DPA
- be adequate, relevant and not excessive in relation to that purpose
- be kept accurate and up-to-date
- not be kept for longer than is necessary for its given purpose

- be subject to appropriate safeguards against unauthorised use, loss or damage.

4. **What is a policy?**

A policy is an official document that gives information about what must be done in your place of work. It sets out the standards that you must achieve, and gives a clear indication of your responsibilities in relation to them.

5. **What is a procedure?**

A procedure is a document that explains how you should do your job ie. it translates policies into working practice. Procedures are based on workplace values and principles to ensure that the job is done properly.